STILL STEAMING

A Guide to Britain's Standard Gauge Steam Railways 2017-2018

EDITOR
John Robinson

Twenty-first Edition

RAILWAY LOCATOR MAP

The numbers shown on this map relate to the page numbers for each railway. Pages 5-6 contain an alphabetical listing of the railways featured in this guide. Please note that the markers on this map show the approximate location only.

3

FOREWORD & ACKNOWLEDGEMENTS

We were greatly impressed by the friendly and cooperative manner of the staff and helpers of the railways which we selected to appear in this book, and wish to thank them for the help they have given. In addition we wish to thank Bob Budd (cover design) and Michael Robinson (page layouts) for their help and also Jonathan James who has provided us with photographs for several railways including the shot used on the cover of this book.

Although we believe that the information contained in this guide is accurate at the time of going to press, we, and the Railways and Museums itemised, are unable to accept liability for any loss, damage, distress or injury suffered as a result of any inaccuracies. Furthermore, we and the Railways are unable to guarantee operating and opening times which may always be subject to cancellation without notice.

We realise that other UK Standard Gauge railways are operating or about to resume operating and we hope to include them in a future edition of Still Steaming.

If you feel we should include other locations or information in future editions, please let us know so that we may give them consideration. We would like to thank you for buying this guide and wish you 'Happy Steaming'!

John Robinson
EDITOR

Note: Further copies of our railway guides, Still Steaming, Little Puffers and Tiny Trains may be obtained, post free, from our address below or ordered on-line via our web site –

www.soccer-books.co.uk

British Library Cataloguing in Publication Data
A catalogue record for this book is available from the British Library

ISBN-13: 978-1-86223-345-4

Copyright © 2017, MARKSMAN PUBLICATIONS. (01472 696226)
72 St. Peter's Avenue, Cleethorpes, N.E. Lincolnshire, DN35 8HU, England

Manufactured in the UK by Ashford Colour Press

COVER PICTURE

The cover image shows ex-United States Army Transportation Corps S100 Class steam locomotive 30065 photographed steaming on the Kent and East Sussex Railway by Jonathan James on 17th July 2016.

CONTENTS

ALDERNEY RAILWAY

Address: P.O. Box 1075, Alderney, Channel Islands GY9 3DA	**N° of Steam Locos**: None at present
Telephone N°: 07911 739572	**N° of Other Locos**: 2
Year Formed: 1978	**N° of Members**: 50
Location of Line: Braye Harbour to Mannez Quarry, Alderney	**Annual Membership Fee**: £15.00
Length of Line: 2 miles	**Approx N° of Visitors P.A.**: 2,000+
	Gauge: Standard
	Web site: www.alderneyrailway.com

Photo courtesy of David Staines

GENERAL INFORMATION

Nearest Mainline Station: Not applicable
Nearest Bus Station: Not applicable
Car Parking: Available on site
Coach Parking: Available on site
Souvenir Shop(s): Yes
Food & Drinks: None at the Railway itself but available nearby

SPECIAL INFORMATION

The original line was built during the 1840s to assist in the construction of the large breakwater in Braye Harbour and fortifications on the island.
The line itself opened in 1847 and was the first nationalised railway run by the Admiralty.

OPERATING INFORMATION

Opening Times: Every Sunday from May until the end of September and also on Saturdays in July and August. An Easter Special operates as does a Santa Special on 18th December 2017. Please contact the railway for further information. Trains usually run at 2.30pm and 3.30pm.
Steam Working: None at present
Prices: Adult Return £5.00
Child Return £3.00

Detailed Directions:
The Railway is situated adjacent to Braye Harbour.

ALN VALLEY RAILWAY

Address: Lionheart Station, Lionheart Enterprise Park, Alnwick NE66 2EX	**Nº of Steam Locos:** 2
Information Line Nº: 0300 030-3311	**Nº of Other Locos:** 5
Year Formed: 1995	**Nº of Members:** 350 approximately
Location: Alnwick, Northumberland	**Approx Nº of Visitors P.A.:** 8,000
Length: 1,300 metres (by June 2017)	**Gauge:** Standard
	Web site: www.alnvalleyrailway.co.uk

GENERAL INFORMATION

Nearest Mainline Station: Alnmouth (5 miles)
Nearest Bus Station: Alnwick (1½ miles)
Car Parking: Available on site
Coach Parking: Available
Souvenir Shop(s): Yes
Food & Drinks: Available

SPECIAL INFORMATION

The Aln Valley Railway Trust has the intention of re-opening the branch line from Alnmouth station, located on the Edinburgh–London main line, through to Alnwick, primarily as a heritage railway attraction. There is also a small museum and model railway room on the site.

OPERATING INFORMATION

Opening Times: 2017 dates: Sundays, Bank Holiday Saturdays and Mondays from 15th April to 24th September (plus 28th & 29th October). Wickham Trolley Rides on 18th & 20th April; 30th May; 25th & 27th July; 1st 3rd, 8th, 10th, 15th, 17th, 22nd & 24th August. Open from 10.30am to 4.30pm on operating days.
Steam Working: 29th & 30th April; 1st & 28th May; 17th & 18th June; 8th, 9th & 30th July; 12th, 13th and 26th to 28th August; 2nd, 3rd, 23rd & 24th September and Santa Specials on 9th, 10th, 13th, 16th & 17th December (pre-booking required)
Prices: Adult Day Ticket £5.00 (Weekdays £4.00)
Child Day Ticket £1.00 (Under-6s free)

Detailed Directions by Car:
Exit the A1 at Willowburn Junction (just to the south of Alnwick) and follow the brown tourist signs marked "Aln Valley Railway" through the Enterprise Park to Lionheart Station. (SatNav users select NE66 2HT) Buses to and from Alnwick Bus Station (services 472 and X15) stop by the Willowburn Filling Station/Sainsbury's store just to the north of the A1. Follow the brown tourist signs on foot from here for the railway.

APPLEBY FRODINGHAM R.P.S.

Address: Appleby Frodingham Railway Preservation Society, c/o Tourist Information Centre, The Buttercross, Market Place, Brigg   DN20 8ER
Telephone N°: (01652) 657053 (bookings)
Year Formed: 1990
Location of Line: British Steel, Scunthorpe

Length of Line: 15 miles used on tours from almost 100 miles of track
N° of Steam Locos: 5
N° of Other Locos: 3
N° of Members: 60
Gauge: Standard
Web site: www.afrps.co.uk

GENERAL INFORMATION

Nearest Mainline Station: Scunthorpe (1 mile)
Nearest Bus Station: Scunthorpe (½ mile)
Car Parking: Large free car park at the site
Coach Parking: At the site
Souvenir Shop(s): Yes – at the Loco Shed
Food & Drinks: Available at the Loco Shed

SPECIAL INFORMATION

The Society operates 15 mile Rail and Brake Van tours of the Scunthorpe steelworks site (which covers almost 12 square miles) using its extensive internal railway system.

OPERATING INFORMATION

Opening Times: Selected weekends throughout the year which <u>must</u> be pre-booked via (01652) 657053 or e-mail – bookings@afrps.co.uk
Private Hire of a train is now available for parties and anniversaries with use of the Lounge coach.
Steam Working: Most active days. Ask for further details when booking.
Prices: Free – but the society relies on donations which are collected at the end of each tour.
Please note that children cannot be carried on Brake Van tours due to the open verandahs.
(Phone 01652 659108 with any enquiries)

Detailed Directions by Car:
Exit the M180 at Junction 4 and take the A18 into Scunthorpe. Turn right at the roundabout by Morrisons supermarket and follow Brigg Road for approximately ½ mile. Turn right into Gate E. Car parking is available on the left and the path to the station is on the right.   SatNav users please enter: DN16 1XA

AVON VALLEY RAILWAY

Address: Bitton Station, Bath Road, Bitton, Bristol BS30 6HD **Telephone Nº**: (0117) 932-5538 **Year Formed**: 1973 **Location of Line**: Midway between Bristol and Bath on A431 **Length of Line**: 3 miles	**Nº of Steam Locos**: 6 **Nº of Other Locos**: 5 **Nº of Members**: Approximately 700 **Annual Membership Fee**: £15.00 **Approx Nº of Visitors P.A.**: 80,000 **Gauge**: Standard **Web site**: www.avonvalleyrailway.org **E-mail**: info@avonvalleyrailway.org

GENERAL INFORMATION

Nearest Mainline Station: Keynsham (1½ miles)
Nearest Bus Station: Bristol or Bath (7 miles)
Car Parking: Available at Bitton Station
Coach Parking: Available at Bitton Station
Souvenir Shop(s): Yes
Food & Drinks: Yes

SPECIAL INFORMATION

The line originally opened in 1869 as a direct route from Birmingham to the south coast but was axed in the 1960s following the Beeching Report. Three miles of track has now been re-laid along the Bristol to Bath section of the line.

OPERATING INFORMATION

Opening Times: 2017 dates: Every Sunday and some Saturdays from 26th March to 29th October and on weekends during December. Also Bank Holiday Mondays, Wednesdays in June and July and Tuesdays to Thursdays during School Holidays. Also open for Santa Specials in December. Open 10.30am to 5.00pm. Please check the web site for further details.
Steam Working: 11.00am to 4.00pm on most days
Prices: Adult £7.00 (£8.00 on Steam Days)
Child £5.00 (£6.00 on Steam Days)
Family Tickets £20.00 (£23.50 Steam Days)
Senior Citizens £6.00 (£7.00 Steam Days)
Note: Special event tickets should be pre-booked.

Detailed Directions by Car:
From All Parts: Exit the M4 at Junction 18. Follow the A46 towards Bath and at the junction with the A420 turn right towards Bristol. At Bridge Yate turn left onto the A4175 and continue until you reach the A431. Turn right and Bitton Station is 100 yards on the right.

BARROW HILL ROUNDHOUSE RAILWAY CENTRE

Address: Barrow Hill Roundhouse, Campbell Drive, Barrow Hill, Staveley, Chesterfield S43 2PR
Telephone Nº: (01246) 472450
Year Formed: 1998
Location: Staveley, near Chesterfield
Length of Line: ¾ mile

Nº of Steam Locos: 12
Nº of Other Locos: Over 40
Nº of Members: Approximately 400
Annual Membership Fee: £22.00 (Adult)
Approx Nº of Visitors P.A.: 30,000
Gauge: Standard
Web site: www.barrowhill.org

GENERAL INFORMATION

Nearest Mainline Station: Chesterfield (3½ miles)
Nearest Bus Station: Chesterfield (3 miles)
Car Parking: Space available for 300 cars
Coach Parking: Available
Souvenir Shop(s): Yes
Food & Drinks: Yes – buffet

SPECIAL INFORMATION

Britain's last remaining operational railway roundhouse provides storage and repair facilities for standard gauge steam, diesel and electric locomotives.

OPERATING INFORMATION

Opening Times: Although the Roundhouse itself will be closed to the general public until an exciting building and renovation project is completed in Autumn 2017, the annual Rail Ale Beer Festival will still take place on 18th, 19th & 20th May when viewing should be possible. Please check the website for further information.
Steam Working: See above.
Prices: Entry is by donation only but charges apply for Special Event days.

Detailed Directions by Car:
Exit the M1 at Junction 30 and take the A619 to Staveley (about 3½ miles). Pass through Staveley, turn right at Troughbrook Road. Continue along for ½ mile, pass under the railway bridge and take the turn immediately on the right. Turn left onto Campbell Drive and the Roundhouse is on the left. The railway is signposted with Brown Tourist signs.

THE BATTLEFIELD LINE

Address: The Battlefield Line, Shackerstone Station, Shackerstone, Warwickshire CV13 6NW **Telephone Nº**: (01827) 880754 **Year Formed**: 1968 **Location of Line**: North West of Market Bosworth **Length of Line**: 5 miles	**Nº of Steam Locos**: 5 **Nº of Other Locos**: 20 **Nº of Members**: 500 approximately **Annual Membership Fee**: £15.00 Adult; £35.00 Family **Approx Nº of Visitors P.A.**: 60,000 **Gauge**: Standard **Web site**: www.battlefieldline.co.uk

GENERAL INFORMATION

Nearest Mainline Station: Nuneaton or Hinckley (both 12 miles)
Nearest Bus Station: Nuneaton & Hinckley (12 miles)
Car Parking: Ample free parking available
Coach Parking: At Market Bosworth Station
Souvenir Shop(s): At Shackerstone Station
Food & Drinks: Yes – Buffets available at all stations

SPECIAL INFORMATION

Travel from the Grade II listed Shackerstone Station through the beautiful Leicestershire countryside with views of the adjoining Ashby Canal. Arrive at the award-winning Shenton Station and explore Bosworth Battlefield (1485) before making the return journey.

OPERATING INFORMATION

Operating Info: 2017 dates: Weekends and Bank Holidays from 18th March to 5th November. Santa Specials on weekends from 25th November to Christmas Eve. Also open from Tuesday to Thursday in July and August, on Wednesdays in June, September & October plus Sundays in November and on 28th December and 1st January 2018. Please check the web site for further details.
Opening Times: 10.00am to 6.00pm
Steam Working: From 11.15am to 4.15pm during high season and 11.00am to 3.30pm at other times.
Prices: Adult Return £11.00   O.A.P. Return £9.00
     Child Return £6.00 (ages 5-15 years)
     Family Ticket £30.00
         (2 adults and 3 children)

Detailed Directions by Car:
Follow the brown tourist signs from the A444 or A447 heading towards the market town of Market Bosworth. Continue towards the villages of Congerstone & Shackerstone and finally to Shackerstone Station. Access is only available via the Old Trackbed.

BEAMISH –
THE LIVING MUSEUM OF THE NORTH

Address: Beamish – The Living Museum of the North, Co. Durham   DH9 0RG
Telephone Nº: (0191) 370-4000
Year Formed: 1970
Length of Line: ½ mile

Nº of Steam Locos: 11
Nº of Other Locos: 3
N.B.: Not all Locos are on display
Approx Nº of Visitors P.A.: 500,000
Web site: www.beamish.org.uk

GENERAL INFORMATION

Nearest Mainline Station: Newcastle Central (8 miles); Durham City (12 miles)
Nearest Bus Station: Newcastle (8 miles); Durham (12 miles)
Car Parking: Free parking for 2,000 cars
Coach Parking: Free parking for 40 coaches
Souvenir Shop(s): Yes
Food & Drinks: Yes – self service tea room, licensed period Public House, Coffee shop and a coal-fired Fish & Chip shop!

SPECIAL INFORMATION

A replica of William Hedley's famous 1813 locomotive "Puffing Billy" steams on the Pockerley Waggonway at Beamish alongside replicas of Locomotion and the Steam Elephant.

OPERATING INFORMATION

Opening Times: Open all year round: from 10.00am to 4.00pm in the Winter (November to March). Closed on Mondays and Fridays in the Winter. Open from 10.00am to 5.00pm during the Summer (April to October). Check for Christmas opening times.
N.B. Mid-week winter visits are centred on the Town, Pit Village and Tramway only. Other areas are closed and admission prices are reduced.
Allow 4-5 hours for a Summer visit and two hours in the Winter.
Steam Working: Daily during the Summer
Prices: Adult £19.00 in Summer
            Child £11.00 in Summer
            Senior Citizen £14.00 in Summer
Children under 5 are admitted free.
Special Family Tickets are available.
Tickets allow unlimited free return visits for 12 months from the date of first visit but are not valid for the Evening events.

Detailed Directions by Car:
From North & South: Follow the A1(M) to Junction 63 (Chester-le-street) and then take A693 for 4 miles towards Stanley; From North-West: Take the A68 south to Castleside near Consett and follow the signs on the A692 and A693 via Stanley.

THE BLUEBELL RAILWAY

Address: The Bluebell Railway, Sheffield Park Station, near Uckfield   TN22 3QL
Telephone Nº: (01825) 720800
Year Formed: 1959
Location: Near Uckfield, East Sussex
Length of Line: 11 miles
Web site: www.bluebell-railway.co.uk

Nº of Steam Locos: Over 30 with up to 3 in operation on any given day
Nº of Other Locos: –
Nº of Members: 10,000
Annual Membership Fee: £25.00 Adult
Approx Nº of Visitors P.A.: 175,000
Gauge: Standard

GENERAL INFORMATION

Nearest Mainline Station: East Grinstead (2 minute walk)
Nearest Bus Station: East Grinstead
Car Parking: Parking is available at Sheffield Park and Horsted Keynes Stations.
Coach Parking: Sheffield Park is best for coaches
Souvenir Shop(s): Yes
Food & Drinks: Yes – buffets and licensed bars & restaurant

SPECIAL INFORMATION

The Railway runs 'Golden Arrow' dining trains on most Saturday evenings and Sunday lunchtimes. There is also a museum at Sheffield Park Station.

OPERATING INFORMATION

Opening Times: 2017 dates: Open every weekend throughout the year and also daily from 1st April to 1st November inclusive. Also open during School holidays and for Santa Specials during December. Open from approximately 10.30am to 5.30pm
Steam Working: As above
Prices: Adult Return £19.00
Child Return £9.50
Family Return £49.00 (2 adult + 3 child)
Note: Prices are cheaper if purchased at least 8 days in advance of a visit.

Detailed Directions by Car:
Sheffield Park Station is situated on the A275 Wych Cross to Lewes road. Horsted Keynes Station is signposted from the B2028 Lingfield to Haywards Heath road.

BODMIN & WENFORD RAILWAY

Address: Bodmin General Station, Losthwithiel Road, Bodmin, Cornwall PL31 1AQ
Telephone N°: (01208) 73555
Year Formed: 1984
Location of Line: Bodmin Parkway to Boscarne Junction, via Bodmin General
Length of Line: 6½ miles

N° of Steam Locos: 11
N° of Other Locos: 9
N° of Members: 1,200
Annual Membership Fee: £18.00
Approx N° of Visitors P.A.: 62,000
Gauge: Standard
Web site: www.bodminrailway.co.uk

GENERAL INFORMATION

Nearest Mainline Station: Bodmin Parkway (cross platform interchange with the Bodmin & Wenford Railway)
Car Parking: Free parking at Bodmin General
Coach Parking: Free parking at Bodmin General
Souvenir Shop(s): Yes
Food & Drinks: Yes

SPECIAL INFORMATION

The Railway has steep gradients and through tickets to "Bodmin & Wenford Railway" are available from all Mainline stations.

OPERATING INFORMATION

Opening Times: 2017 dates: Daily from 16th May to 5th October. Also during various other dates in February, March, April and October (including most weekends). Santa Specials run on 2nd, 3rd, 9th, 10th, 16th, 17th, 21st to 24th, 27th, 28th, 30th and 31st December to 1st January 2018. Open 10.00am–5.00pm on most days. Please contact the railway for details.
Steam Working: Most trains are steam-hauled except for some Saturdays when Heritage diesels are used. Daily steam throughout August.
Prices: Adult All Day Rover £13.00
Senior Citizen All Day Rover £12.00
Child All Day Rover £6.00 (Under-3s free)
Family Day Rover £35.00 (2 adult + 4 child)

Detailed Directions by Car:
From the A30/A38/A389 follow the signs to Bodmin Town Centre then follow the brown tourist signs showing the steam engine logo to the Steam Railway on the B3268 Lostwithiel Road.

BO'NESS & KINNEIL RAILWAY

Address: Bo'ness Station, Union Street, Bo'ness, West Lothian EH51 9AQ **Telephone N°**: (01506) 822298 **Year Opened**: 1981 **Location of Line**: Bo'ness to Manuel **Length of Line**: 5 miles	**N° of Steam Locos**: 26 **Other Locos**: 25 **N° of Members**: 1,500 **Annual Membership Fee**: £22.00 **Approx N° of Visitors P.A.**: 70,000 **Gauge**: Standard **Web site**: www.bkrailway.co.uk

Photo courtesy of Peter Backhouse

GENERAL INFORMATION

Nearest Mainline Station: Linlithgow (3 miles)
Nearest Bus Station: Bo'ness (¼ mile)
Car Parking: Free parking at Bo'ness Station
Coach Parking: Free parking at Bo'ness Station
Souvenir Shop(s): Yes
Food & Drinks: Yes

SPECIAL INFORMATION

In addition to the ten-mile journey, passengers should visit Scotland's largest railway museum at Bo'ness Station. The Railway and Museum are operated by volunteers from The Scottish Railway Preservation Society.

OPERATING INFORMATION

Opening Times: 2017 dates: Weekends from 25th March to 29th October inclusive. Also open for mid-week running on selected dates and most days in July and August. Santa Specials operate on 25th & 26th November plus weekends in December and Hogmanay Black Bun Trains run on 30th & 31st December. The museum is open daily from 25th March to 29th October.
Steam Working: On standard service days, 10.45am, 12.10pm and 2.10pm. The 3.35pm service may be diesel-hauled at weekends.
Prices: Adult Day Ticket £10.00 Child Day £6.00
Family Day Ticket £28.00 Concession Day £9.00
Note: Group discounts are available. Under-5s free. Special fares may apply on Special Event Days.

Detailed Directions by Car:
From Edinburgh: Take the M9 and exit at Junction 3. Then take the A904 to Bo'ness; From Glasgow: Take the M80 to M876 and then M9 (South). Exit at Junction 5 and take A904 to Bo'ness; From the North: Take M9 (South), exit at Junction 5, then take A904 to Bo'ness; From Fife: Leave the A90 after the Forth Bridge, then take A904 to Bo'ness.

BOWES RAILWAY

Address: Bowes Railway, Springwell Village, Gateshead, Tyne & Wear   NE9 7QJ
Telephone Nº: (0191) 416-1847
Year Formed: 1976
Location of Line: Springwell Village
Length of Line: 1¼ miles
Web site: www.bowesrailway.uk

Nº of Steam Locos: 3
Nº of Other Locos: 3 (plus various other colliery locos and diesels)
Nº of Members: Approximately 50
Approx Nº of Visitors P.A.: 5,000
Gauge: Standard

GENERAL INFORMATION

Nearest Mainline Station: Newcastle Central (3 miles)
Nearest Bus Station: Gateshead Interchange (2 miles)
Car Parking: Free parking at site
Coach Parking: Free parking at site
Souvenir Shop(s): Open Tuesday to Saturday throughout the year
Food & Drinks: Available on Event Days only

SPECIAL INFORMATION

Designed by George Stephenson and opened in 1826, the Railway is a scheduled Ancient Monument which operated unique preserved standard gauge rope-hauled inclines and steam hauled passenger trains.

OPERATING INFORMATION

Opening Times: The Springwell site is open for static viewing (no charges) on Tuesdays, Thursdays and Saturdays throughout the year – 10.00am to 4.00pm. The site is also open on the first weekend of each month when an engine is usually in steam.
Steam Working: Usually on the first weekend of each month but please contact the railway directly for further information.
Prices: No specific charges for visiting but donations are requested and admission fees are charged on special event days.

Detailed Directions by Car:
From A1 (Northbound): Follow the A194(M) to the Tyne Tunnel and turn left at the sign for Springwell.
From A1 (Southbound): Take the turn off left for the B1288 to Springwell and Wrekenton.

BRESSINGHAM STEAM EXPERIENCE

Address: Bressingham Steam Museum, Bressingham, Diss, Norfolk   IP22 2AB
Telephone Nº: (01379) 686900
Year Formed: Mid 1950's
Location of Line: Bressingham, Near Diss
Length of Line: 5 miles in total (3 lines)

Nº of Steam Locos: 6 Standard gauge plus many others
Approx Nº of Visitors P.A.: 80,000+
Gauge: Standard, 2 foot, 10¼ inches and 15 inches
Web site: www.bressingham.co.uk

GENERAL INFORMATION

Nearest Mainline Station: Diss (2½ miles)
Nearest Bus Station: Bressingham (1¼ miles)
Car Parking: Free parking for 400 cars available
Coach Parking: Free parking for 30 coaches
Souvenir Shop(s): Yes
Food & Drinks: Yes

SPECIAL INFORMATION

In addition to Steam locomotives, Bressingham has a large selection of steam traction engines, fixed steam engines and also the National Dad's Army Museum, two extensive gardens and a water garden centre.

OPERATING INFORMATION

Opening Times: 2017 dates: Daily from 27th March to 29th October. Open from 10.30am to 5.00pm and until 5.30pm in June, July and August and until 4.30pm in October.
Steam Working: Almost every operating day except for most (but not all) Mondays and Tuesdays in April, May, June, July, September and October. Please contact the Museum for further details.
Prices: Adult £11.99 (non-Steam) £14.75 (Steam)
Child £7.99 (non-Steam) £9.99 (Steam)
Seniors £10.99 (non-Steam) £13.50 (Steam)
Note: Reduced entry charges are available for visitors who do not take railway rides. The prices shown include an optional donation of 10%.

Detailed Directions by Car:
From All Parts: Take the A11 to Thetford and then follow the A1066 towards Diss for Bressingham. The Museum is signposted by the brown tourist signs.   SATNAV please use the following post code: IP22 2AA

BRISTOL HARBOUR RAILWAY

Address: Princes Wharf, City Docks, Bristol BS1 4RN	**Length of Line**: 1½ miles
Telephone Nº: (0117) 352-6600	**Nº of Steam Locos**: 2
Year Formed: 1978	**Nº of Other Locos**: 1
Location of Line: South side of the Floating Harbour	**Gauge**: Standard
	Web site: mshed.org

GENERAL INFORMATION

Nearest Mainline Station: Bristol Temple Meads (1 mile)
Nearest Bus Station: City Centre (½ mile)
Car Parking: Pay & Display adjacent to M Shed
Coach Parking: Pay & Display adjacent
Souvenir Shop(s): In the M Shed Museum
Food & Drinks: Café in the Museum

SPECIAL INFORMATION

The new M Shed museum opened in June 2011 and has since attracted over 1 million visitors. Trains run alongside the harbour to link M Shed with the SS Great Britain on the dockside and from M Shed to Ashton Bridge along the New Cut, giving a choice of scenery on alternate routes.

OPERATING INFORMATION

Opening Times: 2017 dates: 8th, 9th, 15th, 16th & 29th April; 1st, 13th, 14th and 27th to 29th May; 10th, 11th, 24th & 25th June; 8th, 99th, 22nd, 23rd, 29th & 30th July; 12th, 13th, 26th & 27th August; 9th, 10th, 23rd & 24th September; 7th, 8th, 21st, 22nd, 28th & 29th October. Trains run from 11.00am to 4.00pm or 5.00pm.
Steam Working: Please contact the railway for further details.
Prices: All-day Rover £4.00
M Shed to Vauxhall Bridge Return £4.00
M Shed to SS Great Britain Return £3.00
M Shed to SS Great Britain Single £2.00
Note: Children under the age of 6 travel for free.

Detailed Directions by Car:
From All Parts: Follow signs to Bristol City Centre and then the Brown Tourist signs for the Museum. A good landmark to look out for are the 4 huge quayside cranes.

BUCKINGHAMSHIRE RAILWAY CENTRE

Address: Quainton Road Station, Quainton, Aylesbury, Bucks. HP22 4BY	**Nº of Steam Locos**: 30
Telephone Nº: (01296) 655720	**Nº of Other Locos**: 6
Year Formed: 1969	**Nº of Members**: 1,000
	Annual Membership Fee: £25.00
Location of Line: At Quainton on the old Metropolitan/Great Central Line	**Approx Nº of Visitors P.A.**: 35,000
	Gauge: Standard (also a Miniature line)
Length of Line: 2 × ½ mile demo tracks	**Recorded Info. Line**: (01296) 655450

GENERAL INFORMATION

Nearest Mainline Station: Aylesbury (6 miles)
Nearest Bus Station: Aylesbury
Car Parking: Free parking for 500 cars available
Coach Parking: Free parking for 10 coaches
Souvenir Shop(s): Yes
Food & Drinks: Yes

SPECIAL INFORMATION

In addition to a large collection of locomotives and carriages, the Centre has an extensive ½ mile outdoor miniature railway system operated by the Vale of Aylesbury Model Engineering Society.

Web site: www.bucksrailcentre.org
E-mail: office@bucksrailcentre.org

OPERATING INFORMATION

Opening Times: 2017 dates: Tuesday to Thursday for restricted viewing only from 4th April to 31st October. Trains run on Sundays and Bank Holidays from 2nd April to 29th October. Also on Wednesdays from 12th July to 30th August and some other Special Event days including December weekends.
Steam Working: All operating days.
Prices: Adult £6.00, £11.00 and £13.00
  Child £4.00, £8.00 and £10.00
    (Under 5's travel free of charge)
  Senior Citizen £5.00, £10.00 and £12.00
  Family £17.00, £32.00 and £38.00
    (2 adults + up to 4 children)
Note: Prices shown above are for restricted viewing, Steam Days and Special Event days respectively. 'Thomas' Days are more expensive still.

Detailed Directions by Car:
The Buckinghamshire Railway Centre is signposted off the A41 Aylesbury to Bicester Road at Waddesdon and off the A413 Buckingham to Aylesbury road at Whitchurch. Junctions 7, 8 and 9 of the M40 are all close by.

CALEDONIAN RAILWAY

Address: The Station, Park Road, Brechin, Angus DD9 7AF	**N° of Steam Locos**: 5 **Other Locos**: 10
Telephone N°: (01356) 622992 (Available on operating days only)	**N° of Members**: 250
Year Formed: 1979	**Annual Membership Fee**: Adult £15.00; Family £25.00; Senior £12.00; Junior £6
Location: Brechin to the Bridge of Dun	**Approx N° of Visitors P.A.**: 12,000
Length of Line: 4 miles	**Gauge**: Standard
	Web site: www.caledonianrailway.com

GENERAL INFORMATION

Nearest Mainline Station: Montrose (4½ miles)
Nearest Bus Station: Brechin (200 yards)
Car Parking: Ample free parking at both Stations
Coach Parking: Free parking at both Stations
Souvenir Shop(s): Yes
Food & Drinks: Light refreshments are available

SPECIAL INFORMATION

Brechin Station is the only original Terminus station in preservation.

OPERATING INFORMATION

Opening Times: 2017 dates: Easter Sundays, Santa Specials on some weekends in December, every Sunday from 4th June to 10th September and Diesel services on Saturdays in July and August. Also open for some other Special Events throughout the year. Please check the web site for further details. Trains usually run from 11.00am to 3.00pm.
Steam Working: Steam service on every operating Sunday in addition to other Special Events days.
Prices: Adult Return £8.00
           Child Return £6.00 (Under-3s free)
           Senior Citizen Return £7.00
           Family Return £25.00 (2 Adult + 3 Child)
Higher fares may apply for Special Event days and All Day tickets are also available.

Detailed Directions by Car:
From South: For Brechin Station, leave the A90 at the Brechin turn-off and go straight through the Town Centre. Pass the Northern Hotel, take the 2nd exit at the mini-roundabout then it is 150 yards to Park Road/St. Ninian Square; From North: For Brechin Station, leave the A90 at the Brechin turn-off and go straight through Trinity Village. Turn left at the mini-roundabout, it is then 250 yards to Park Road/St. Ninian Square. Bridge of Dun is situated half way between Brechin and Montrose. (Follow tourist signs).

CAMBRIAN HERITAGE RAILWAYS

Address: Old Station Building, Oswald Street, Oswestry SY11 4RE **Telephone No**: (01691) 728131 **Year Formed**: 2009 **Location of Line**: Llynclys and Oswestry **Length of Line**: Almost 1 mile at each site	**No of Steam Locos**: 4 (under repair) **No of Other Locos**: 2 DMUs + 7 others **No of Members**: 500+ **Annual Membership Fee**: £15.00 **Approx No of Visitors P.A.**: 15,000 **Gauge**: Standard **Web site**: www.cambrianrailways.com

GENERAL INFORMATION

Nearest Mainline Station: Gobowen (3 miles from Oswestry – 7 miles from Llynclys)
Nearest Bus Station: Oswestry
Car Parking: Available at both sites
Coach Parking: Please contact the railway's Coach Tour officer for further information.
Souvenir Shop(s): Yes
Food & Drinks: Available

SPECIAL INFORMATION

Cambrian Heritage Railways currently operate at two separate sites along the 8½ mile Gobowen to Llanyblodwel line. The short to medium term aim is to link the two sites to make a 6 mile long heritage railway and the CHR is currently extending the operational line as Oswestry towards Llynclys.

OPERATING INFORMATION

Opening Times: 2017 dates: Open every Saturday, Sunday and Bank Holiday from 25th March to 29th October and also on some other dates. Please check the web site for further information.
Trains run from 11.00am to 4.00pm at Llynclys and until 3.00pm at Oswestry.
Steam Working: Hired steam locos operate at peak times. Please check the website for further details.
Prices: Adults £4.50
Concessions £3.50
Children £2.50
Family £11.00 (2 adults + 2 children)
Note: All the above prices are for "Full Day Rover" tickets on Diesel-hauled days. Higher fares may apply on Steam-hauled days.

Detailed Directions by Car:
The Llynclys site is situated on the B4396 approximately 5 miles southwest of Oswestry, just off the A483 heading towards Welshpool. Turn left at Llyncly Crossroads towards Knockin. The entrance to the site is on the right after about 400 yards, immediately over the railway bridge. The Oswestry site is near the town centre and is clearly signposted.

CHASEWATER RAILWAY (THE COLLIERY LINE)

Address: Chasewater Country Park,
Pool Lane, Burntwood, Staffs,
WS8 7NL
Telephone Nº: (01543) 452623
Year Re-formed: 1985
Location: Chasewater Country Park, near
Brownhills, Walsall
Length of Line: 2 miles

Nº of Steam Locos: 12 (4 in service)
Nº of Other Locos: 15 (3 in service)
Approx Nº of Visitors P.A.: 45,000
Gauge: Standard
Web site: www.chasewaterrailway.co.uk

GENERAL INFORMATION

Nearest Mainline Station: Walsall or Cannock
(both approximately 8 miles)
Nearest Bus Station: Lichfield (8½ miles)
Car Parking: Free parking in Chasewater Park
Coach Parking: Free parking in Chasewater Park
Souvenir Shop(s): Yes
Food & Drinks: Yes

SPECIAL INFORMATION

Chasewater Railway is based on the Cannock Chase
& Wolverhampton Railway opened in 1856. The
railway passed into the hands of the National Coal
Board which ceased using the line in 1965.
Trains operate between Brownhills West and
Chasetown.

OPERATING INFORMATION

Opening Times: 2017 dates: Sundays and Bank
Holiday Mondays from 5th March to 12th
November plus Saturdays from Easter to 7th
October and selected mid-week operating days.
Please check the web site for further details. Also
Santa Specials in December. A regular service runs
from 11.00am on operating days.
Steam Working: Please check the web site or phone
the railway for further details.
Prices: Adult Return £5.95
Child Return £3.95 (Under-3s ride free)
Concession Return £4.95
Family Return £16.95
All tickets offer unlimited rides on the day of issue.

Detailed Directions by Car:
Chasewater Country Park is situated in Brownhills off the A5 southbound near the junction of the A5 with the
A452 Chester Road. Follow the Brown tourist signs on the A5 for the Country Park.

CHATHAM HISTORIC DOCKYARD RAILWAY

Address: Dock Road, Chatham
Telephone Nº: (01634) 823800
Year Formed: 2001
Location of Line: Chatham, Kent
Length of Line: ¾ mile

Nº of Steam Locos: 5
Nº of Other Locos: 3
Gauge: Standard and also 18 inches
Web site: www.dockyardrailway.co.uk

GENERAL INFORMATION

Nearest Mainline Station: Chatham (1½ miles)
Nearest Bus Station: Gillingham (1½ miles)
Car Parking: Available on site
Coach Parking: Available
Souvenir Shop(s): Yes
Food & Drinks: Available

SPECIAL INFORMATION

The Dockyard Railway is operated by North Kent
Industrial Locomotive Society and runs
demonstrations of freight steaming at Chatham's
Historic Dockyard (www.chdt.org.uk).

OPERATING INFORMATION

Opening Times: 2017 dates: 1st, 2nd, 16th & 17th
April; 6th & 7th May; 18th June; 22nd & 23rd July;
12th, 13th, 26th & 27th August; 9th, 10th, 16th &
17th September; 21st, 22nd, 28th & 29th October.
Steam Working: Most operating days. Please note
that the Railway does not offer train rides, merely
demonstrations of engines in operation.
Prices: Adults £24.00
            Children (Aged 5-15 years old) £14.00
            Concessions £21.50
            Family Tickets £63.00
Note: Prices shown are for admission to the
Dockyard and tickets are valid for 12 months.
However, entrance to some special events is an
additional charge.

Detailed Directions by Car:
From All Parts: Exit the M2 at Junction 3 and follow the A229 to Chatham. Follow the Brown tourist signs which
clearly mark the correct route to the Dockyard.

CHINNOR & PRINCES RISBOROUGH RAILWAY

Address: Station Road, Chinnor, Oxon, OX39 4ER
Telephone Nº: (01844) 353535 (timetable)
Year Formed: 1989
Location: The Icknield Line, Chinnor
Length of Line: 3½ miles
Gauge: Standard

Nº of Steam Locos: 1
Nº of Other Locos: 6
Nº of Members: 1,000
Annual Membership Fee: Adult £20.00; Family £35.00; Child £10.00; OAP £15.00
Approx Nº of Visitors P.A.: 15,000
Web Site: www.chinnorrailway.co.uk

GENERAL INFORMATION

Nearest Mainline Station: Princes Risborough (4 miles)
Nearest Bus Station: High Wycombe (10 miles)
Car Parking: Free parking at site
Coach Parking: Prior arrangement preferred but not necessary
Souvenir Shop(s): Yes
Food & Drinks: Soft drinks and light snacks in Station Buffet. Buffet usually available on trains.

SPECIAL INFORMATION

The Chinnor & Princes Risborough Railway operates the remaining 3½ mile section of the former GWR Watlington Branch from Chinnor to Thame Junction.

OPERATING INFORMATION

Opening Times: 2017 dates: Sundays and Bank Holiday Mondays from 2nd April to 29th October and also Santa Specials on weekends in December plus Mince Pie Specials between Christmas and New Year's Eve. Please check the railway's website for details of other bookable special and evening events during the year.
Steam Working: Operates from 11.00am to 4.30pm on Sundays and Bank Holidays
Prices: Adult Return £11.00 Child Return £6.00
 Family Return £28.00 (2 adult + 2 child)
 Senior Citizen Return £10.00
Note: Discounts are available for advance purchases

Detailed Directions by Car:
From All Parts: The railway at Chinnor is situated in Station Road just off the B4009. Junction 6 of the M40 is 4 miles away and Princes Risborough 4 miles further along the B4009. Once in Chinnor follow the brown Tourist signs to the railway.

CHOLSEY & WALLINGFORD RAILWAY

Address: Wallingford Station, 5 Hithercroft Road, Wallingford, Oxon, OX10 9GQ	**N° of Steam Locos**: Visiting locos only
	N° of Other Locos: 4
	N° of Members: 250
Telephone N°: (01491) 835067 (24hr info)	**Annual Membership Fee**: £14.00
Year Formed: 1981	**Approx N° of Visitors P.A.**: 9,700
Location of Line: Wallingford, Oxon.	**Gauge**: Standard
Length of Line: 2½ miles	**Web**: www.cholsey-wallingford-railway.com

GENERAL INFORMATION

Nearest Mainline Station: Joint station at Cholsey
Nearest Bus Station: Wallingford (¼ mile)
Car Parking: Off road parking available
Coach Parking: Off road parking available
Souvenir Shop(s): Yes
Food & Drinks: Yes

SPECIAL INFORMATION

The Wallingford branch (now known as "The Bunk Line") was originally intended as a through line to Princes Risborough, via Watlington, but became the first standard gauge branch of Brunel's broad-gauge London to Bristol line.

OPERATING INFORMATION

Opening Times: Selected weekends from Easter until Christmas with trains running from 11.00am to 4.30pm – please phone the railway or check the web site for further details.

Steam Working: The railway will have visiting steam locomotives from time to time. Please contact the railway for further information.

Prices: Adult Return £8.00 (£6.00 diesel days)
         Child Return £4.50 (£3.50 diesel days)
         Concessionary Return £6.50 (£5.00 diesel)
         Family Return £23.00 (£17.00 diesel days)
                    (2 adults + 2 children)

Prices: Prices may be subject to change for Engine visits and other special events.

Detailed Directions by Car:
From All Parts: Exit from the A34 at the Milton Interchange (between E. Ilsley and Abingdon). Follow signs to Didcot and Wallingford (A4130). Take Wallingford bypass, then turn left at the first roundabout (signposted Hithercroft Road). The Station is then ½ mile on the right.

CHURNET VALLEY RAILWAY

Address: Kingsley & Froghall Station, Froghall, Stoke-on-Trent ST10 2HA	**N° of Steam Locos**: 6 (2 in operation)
Telephone N°: (01538) 750755	**N° of Other Locos**: 11 (3 in operation)
Year Formed: 1978	**Approx N° of Visitors P.A.**: 70,000
Location of Line: Kingsley & Froghall to Cheddleton	**Gauge**: Standard
	Web: www.churnet-valley-railway.co.uk

Length: 5¼ miles (plus a further 8 miles when operating on the Cauldon Branch)

Photo courtesy of D.R. Gibson

GENERAL INFORMATION

Nearest Mainline Station: Stoke-on-Trent (12 miles)
Nearest Bus Station: Leek (5 miles)
Car Parking: Parking available on site
Coach Parking: Restricted space available at Kingsley & Froghall Station.
Souvenir Shop(s): Yes
Food & Drinks: Yes

SPECIAL INFORMATION

Cheddleton Station is a Grade II listed building, Consall is a sleepy halt with Victorian charm, whereas Kingsley & Froghall has been rebuilt in NSR style and includes disabled facilities and a tearoom.

OPERATING INFORMATION

Opening Times: 2017 dates: Sundays from 2nd April until 22nd October; most Saturdays during April, May, June, July and August; Every Wednesday from June to August and all Bank Holiday Mondays. Santa Specials run on weekends and Wednesdays in December (pre-booking required). Please check the web site or contact the railway for timetable details and any other information.

Steam Working: Most operating days except for Diesel Gala days.

Prices: Adult Day Rover £12.00 to £17.00
Child Day Rover £6.00 – £11.00 (Age 4-14)
Senior Citizen Day Rover £10.00 to £15.00
Family Ticket Day Rover £30.00 to £48.00

Detailed Directions by Car:
From All Parts: Take the M6 to Stoke-on-Trent and follow roads to Ashbourne or Leek. Cheddleton Station is off the A520 Leek to Stone road (SatNav ST13 7EE). Kingsley & Froghall Station is off the A52 Ashbourne Road.

COLEFORD GWR MUSEUM

Address: The Old Railway Station, Railway Drive, Coleford GL16 8RH
Telephone Nº: (01594) 833569
Year Formed: 1988
Location of Line: Coleford
Length of Line: 100 yards

Nº of Steam Locos: 1
Nº of Other Locos: 2 (7¼ inches)
Approx Nº of Visitors P.A.: Not known
Gauge: 7¼ inches and Standard gauge
Web site: None

GENERAL INFORMATION

Nearest Mainline Station: Lydney (7½ miles)
Nearest Bus Station: Gloucester (20 miles)
Car Parking: Low cost parking available on site
Coach Parking: Not available
Souvenir Shop(s): No souvenirs but a number of railway books are available for purchase.
Food & Drinks: Tea and Coffee available only

SPECIAL INFORMATION

Based in the 1883 Goods Shed at Coleford, the Museum chronicles the history of railways in the Forest of Dean.

OPERATING INFORMATION

Opening Times: 2017 dates: Friday and Saturday afternoons and Bank Holidays throughout the year. Open from 2.30pm to 5.00pm.
Steam Working: The standard gauge loco is not currently in service but steam rides are available on the two 7¼ inch locos.
Prices: Adults £4.00 (admission to the museum)
  Children £2.00 (admission to the museum)
  Miniature Railway Rides £2.00
  Peckett Footplate Visit £2.00 (if steaming)

Detailed Directions by Car:
From All Parts: From the M50 take the A40 at Ross-on-Wye to Monmouth then the A4136 towards Cinderford. Turn off the A4136 into Coleford and the Museum is located in the Town Centre.

COLNE VALLEY RAILWAY

Address: Castle Hedingham Station, Yeldham Road, Castle Hedingham, Essex, CO9 3DZ	**N⁰ of Steam Locos**: 7
	N⁰ of Other Locos: 11
	Approx N⁰ of Visitors P.A.: 45,000
Telephone N⁰: (01787) 461174	**Gauge**: Standard and 7¼ inches
Year Formed: 1974	**Web Site**: www.colnevalleyrailway.co.uk
Location: 7 miles north-west of Braintree	
Length of Line: Approximately 1 mile	

GENERAL INFORMATION

Nearest Mainline Station: Braintree (7 miles)
Nearest Bus Station: Hedingham bus from Braintree stops at the Railway (except on Sundays)
Car Parking: Parking at the site
Coach Parking: Free parking at site
Souvenir Shop(s): Yes
Food & Drinks: Yes – on operational days. Also Pullman Sunday Lunches – bookings necessary.

SPECIAL INFORMATION

The railway has been re-built on a section of the old Colne Valley & Halstead Railway, with all buildings, bridges, signal boxes, etc. re-located on site.

OPERATING INFORMATION

Opening Times: 2017 dates: Steam trains run every Sunday and Bank Holiday weekend from 2nd April to 22nd October and on Wednesdays during the School Holidays. Diesel trains run on Thursdays during School Holidays and some Saturdays. Pre-booked parties by arrangement and various other special events. Check the web site for details.
Steam Working: Site opens at 10.30am. Trains run from 11.30am. Last admission at 3.30pm.
Prices: Adult – Steam days £10.00; Diesel £8.00
Child – Steam £5.00; Diesel £4.00
Family (2 adults + 3 children) –
Steam £27.50; Diesel £22.00
Senior Citizen – Steam £7.50; Diesel £6.00

Detailed Directions by Car:
Exit the M11 at Junction 8 (Stanstead Airport) and follow the A120 eastwards to Braintree. Take the A131 northwards to High Garrett and bear left at the traffic lights onto the A1017 signposted Haverhill. Follow this road for 6 miles and the entrance to the railway is on the right past the villages of Gosfield and Sible Hedingham.

CREWE HERITAGE CENTRE

Address: Vernon Way, Crewe, CW1 2DB
Telephone Nº: (01270) 212130
Year Formed: 1987
Location of Line: Crewe Heritage Centre
Length of Line: 300 yards (Standard gauge) and 600 yards (7¼ inch gauge)

Nº of Steam Locos: 1
Nº of Other Locos: 2
Approx Nº of Visitors P.A.: 10,000
Gauge: 7¼ inches and Standard Gauge
Web site: www.creweheritagecentre.org

GENERAL INFORMATION

Nearest Mainline Station: Crewe (¾ mile)
Nearest Bus Station: Crewe (½ mile)
Car Parking: Available on site
Coach Parking: None
Souvenir Shop(s): Yes
Food & Drinks: Tea and Coffee only

SPECIAL INFORMATION

Crewe Heritage Centre is an operational base for numerous mainline steam charters with various locomotives present throughout the year.

OPERATING INFORMATION

Opening Times: Weekends and Bank Holidays from April until the end of September. Open 10.00am to 4.30pm with last admissions at 3.30pm.
Steam Working: Please contact the Centre for details.
Prices: Adults £5.00
Children £3.00
Concessions £3.00
Family Tickets £10.00

Detailed Directions by Car:
From All Parts: Exit the M6 at Junction 16 and take the A500 into Crewe. Follow the brown tourist signs for "The Railway Age". The Heritage Centre is adjacent to Crewe Railway Station and next to the Tesco Supermarket.

THE DARTMOOR RAILWAY

Address: Okehampton Station, Station Road, Okehampton EX20 1EJ **Telephone Nº:** (01837) 55164 **Year Formed:** 1997 **Location of Line:** Meldon to Okehampton	**Length of Line:** 15½ miles (Heritage service operates on 3½ miles of the line) **Nº of Steam Locos:** Visiting locos only **Nº of Other Locos:** 2 and DMUs **Gauge:** Standard **Web site:** www.dartmoor-railway-sa.org

GENERAL INFORMATION

Nearest Mainline Station: Crediton
Nearest Bus Station: Okehampton
Car Parking: Okehampton Station and some spaces at Sampford Courtenay Station – all free of charge
Coach Parking: Okehampton Station
Souvenir Shop(s): Yes
Food & Drinks: Okehampton Buffet and Meldon Buffet are open on Bank Holidays and other operating days. The Buffets are fully licensed.

SPECIAL INFORMATION

The railway operates on the route of the old Southern Railway line through the mid-Devon countryside to the northern slopes of Dartmoor National Park.

OPERATING INFORMATION

Opening Times: 2017 heritage services will operate on weekends and Bank Holidays from Good Friday until September, departing Okehampton hourly from 10.30am to 4.00pm.
Steam Working: Please contact the railway for further information.
Prices: Adult £5.00 (Day rover ticket)
Concession £4.00 (Day rover ticket)
Child (ages 5 to 15) £3.00 (Day rover ticket)
Under-5s travel free of charge
Family Ticket £14.00 (2 adult + 2 children)

Detailed Directions by Car:
From All Parts: Take the A30 Exeter to Launceston dual carriageway and exit at the Okehampton turn-off. Once in town, follow the brown tourist signs up the hill to Okehampton Station.

DARTMOUTH STEAM RAILWAY & RIVER BOAT COMPANY

Address: Queen's Park Station, Torbay Road, Paignton   TQ4 6AF
Telephone Nº: (01803) 555872
E-mail: carolyn@dsrrb.co.uk
Year Formed: 1973
Location of Line: Paignton to Kingswear
Length of Line: 7 miles

Nº of Steam Locos: 4
Nº of Other Locos: 1
Approx Nº of Visitors P.A.: 350,000
Gauge: Standard
Web site: www.dartmouthrailriver.co.uk

GENERAL INFORMATION

Nearest Mainline Station: Paignton (adjacent)
Nearest Bus Station: Paignton (2 minutes walk)
Car Parking: Multi-storey or Mainline Station
Coach Parking: Multi-storey (3 minutes walk)
Souvenir Shop(s): Yes – at Paignton & Kingswear
Food & Drinks: Yes – at Paignton & Kingswear

SPECIAL INFORMATION

A passenger ferry is available from Kingswear Station across to Dartmouth. Combined excursions are also available including train and river trips.

OPERATING INFORMATION

Opening Times: 2017 dates: Open daily from 1st April to 28th October and on other dates in February and November. Santa Specials operate during dates in December. Please contact the railway for further information.
Steam Working: Trains run throughout the day from 10.30am to 5.00pm.
Prices: Adult Return £16.75 (Includes ferry charge)
Child Return £10.00 (Includes ferry charge)
Concession Return £15.75 (Includes ferry)
Family Return £45.50
(2 adults and 2 children – Includes ferry charge)
Note: Cheaper fares are charged for shorter journeys

Detailed Directions by Car:
From All Parts: Take the M5 to Exeter and then the A380 to Paignton.

DEAN FOREST RAILWAY

Address: Norchard Centre, Forest Road; Lydney, Gloucestershire   GL15 4ET
Telephone Nº: (01594) 845840
Information Line: (01594) 843423 (24 hr.)
Year Formed: 1970
Location of Line: Lydney, Gloucestershire
Length of Line: 4½ miles

Nº of Steam Locos: 7 (2 in service)
Nº of Other Locos: 18 (3 in service)
Nº of Members: 1,000
Annual Membership Fee: Adult £14.00; Family (4 persons) £17.00
Approx Nº of Visitors P.A.: 35,000
Gauge: Standard
Web site: www.deanforestrailway.co.uk

GENERAL INFORMATION

Nearest Mainline Station: Lydney (200 metres)
Nearest Bus Station: Lydney Town (400 metres)
Car Parking: 600 spaces available at Norchard
Coach Parking: Ample space available
Souvenir Shop(s): Yes + a Museum
Food & Drinks: Yes – on operational days only

SPECIAL INFORMATION

Dean Forest Railway preserves the sole surviving line of the Severn and Wye Railway. The Railway has lengthened the line to a total of 4½ miles and Norchard to Parkend is now open for steam train operation giving a round trip of 9 miles.

OPERATING INFORMATION

Opening Times: 2017 dates: Norchard is open every day for viewing. Trains operate on Sundays from 5th March to 26th November, on Wednesdays and Saturdays from 5th March to 28th October and various other dates including Santa Specials in December. Please contact the railway for further details.
Steam Working: Most services are steam-hauled – check the web site or phone for details. Trains depart Norchard at various times from 10.35am to 3.30pm.
Prices: Adult Return £12.00   OAP Return £11.00
          Child Return £6.00 (Under-5s free)
          Family Ticket £32.00 (2 adults + 2 children)
Note: Fares may differ on Special Event days.

Detailed Directions by Car:
From M50 & Ross-on-Wye: Take the B4228 and B4234 via Coleford to reach Lydney. Norchard is located on the B4234, ¾ mile north of Lydney Town Centre; From Monmouth: Take the A4136 and B4431 onto the B4234 via Coleford; From South Wales: Take the M4 then M48 onto the A48 via Chepstow to Lydney; From Midlands/ Gloucester: Take the M5 to Gloucester then the A48 to Lydney; From the West Country: Take the M4 and M48 via the 'Old' Severn Bridge to Chepstow and then the A48 to Lydney.

DERWENT VALLEY LIGHT RAILWAY
(THE BLACKBERRY LINE)

Address: Murton Park, Murton Lane, Murton, York   YO19 5UF
Telephone Nº: (01904) 489966
Year Formed: 1991
Location of Line: Murton, near York
Length of Line: ½ mile
Web site: www.dvlr.org.uk

Nº of Steam Locos: 1
Nº of Other Locos: 9
Nº of Members: 148
Annual Membership Fee: £16.00
Approx Nº of Visitors P.A.: 12,000
Gauge: Standard
E-mail: dvlr@hotmail.co.uk

GENERAL INFORMATION

Nearest Mainline Station: York (4 miles)
Nearest Bus Station: York (4 miles)
Car Parking: Large free car park at the site
Coach Parking: Free at the site
Souvenir Shop(s): Yes
Food & Drinks: Available in the Museum.

SPECIAL INFORMATION

The site is the remnants of the Derwent Valley Light Railway which was the last privately owned railway in England, originally opened in 1913.

OPERATING INFORMATION

Opening Times: 2017 dates: Sundays, Bank Holidays and some Saturdays from 16th April until 24th September. Open from 11.00am to 4.15pm. Santa Specials also operate on dates in December.
Steam Working: None during 2017.
Prices: Adult £6.50   Child £4.50
            Senior Citizens/Students £5.50
            Family Tickets £18.00 (2 adult + 2 children)
Note: Prices shown are for entry to the museum. Rides are free thereafter. Prices may be higher on some Special Event days.

Detailed Directions by Car:
From All Parts: The railway is well signposted for the Yorkshire Museum of Farming from the A64 (York to Scarborough road), the A1079 (York to Hull road) and the A166 (York to Bridlington road).

DIDCOT RAILWAY CENTRE

Address: Didcot Railway Centre, Didcot, Oxfordshire OX11 7NJ	**N⁰ of Steam Locos:** 23
Telephone N⁰: (01235) 817200	**N⁰ of Other Locos:** 2
Year Formed: 1961	**N⁰ of Members:** 4,400
Location of Line: Didcot	**Annual Membership Fee:** Full £26.00; Over 60/Under 18 £18.00; Family £33.00
Length of Line: ¾ mile	**Approx N⁰ of Visitors P.A.:** 70,000
Gauge: Standard and 7 foot ¼ inch	**Web Site:** www.didcotrailwaycentre.org.uk

GENERAL INFORMATION

Nearest Mainline Station: Didcot Parkway (adjacent)
Nearest Bus Station: Buses to Didcot call at the Railway station
Car Parking: BR car park adjacent
Coach Parking: As above
Souvenir Shop(s): Yes
Food & Drinks: Yes

SPECIAL INFORMATION

The Centre is based on a Great Western Railway engine shed and is devoted to the re-creation of part of the GWR including Brunel's broad gauge railway and a newly built replica of the Fire Fly locomotive of 1840.

OPERATING INFO

Opening Times: 2017 dates: Weekends all year round, open daily during most school holidays and also from 27th May to 10th September. Weekends and Steam days open 10.30am to 5.00pm. Other days and during the Winter, open 10.30am to 3.30pm.
Steam Working: Bank Holidays and every weekend from 3rd June until 3rd September and Wednesdays from 26th July to 30th August. Please phone or check the web site for details of Autumn steam days.
Prices: Adult £5.50–£15.00
Child £4.50–£16.00
Senior Citizen £5.00–£13.00
Discounted family tickets are available (2 adults + 2 children) except for Thomas days and other special events. Prices vary depending on the events.

Detailed Directions by Car:
From East & West: Take the M4 to Junction 13 then the A34 and A4130 (follow brown Tourist signs to Didcot Railway Centre); From North: The Centre is signed from the A34 to A4130.

DOWNPATRICK & COUNTY DOWN RAILWAY

Address: Market Street, Downpatrick, Co. Down, Northern Ireland
Telephone N°: 028 4461 5779
Year Formed: 1985
Location of Line: Downpatrick
Length of Line: 2 miles
Gauge: Irish Standard (5 foot 3 inches)

N° of Steam Locos: 3
N° of Other Locos: 5
N° of Members: 200
Annual Membership Fee: Adult £25.00, Family £50.00, Concessions £20.00
Approx N° of Visitors P.A.: 13,000
Web: www.downrail.co.uk

GENERAL INFORMATION

Nearest Mainline Station: –
Nearest Bus Station: Adjacent to Station
Car Parking: Ample parking adjacent to Station
Coach Parking: Ample parking adjacent to Station
Souvenir Shop(s): Yes
Food & Drinks: Yes

SPECIAL INFORMATION

This is the only operating Standard (5' 3") Gauge Heritage Railway in Ireland. A carriage Viewing Gallery has recently been opened to enable visitors to get a close-up view of the operations carried out by the Society members.

OPERATING INFORMATION

Opening Times: The Museum is open daily from June to September.
Steam Working: 2017 dates: Easter and May Bank Holiday weekends then weekends from 17th June to 10th September. Also Halloween Ghost Trains on dates in October and Santa and Mince Pie Specials on some dates in December. Please contact the railway for further details. Trains usually run from 2.00pm to 5.00pm.
Prices: Adult Return £6.00
 Child Return £4.50 (Under-3's ride free)
 Concessionary Return £5.50
 Family Return £18.00

Detailed Directions by Car:
From Belfast take the A7 Downpatrick Road. Upon arrival in Downpatrick, follow the brown tourist signs and the Railway Museum is adjacent to the bus station.

EAST ANGLIAN RAILWAY MUSEUM

Address: Chappel & Wakes Colne Station, Colchester, Essex   CO6 2DS
Telephone Nº: (01206) 242524
Year Formed: 1969
Location of Line: 6 miles west of Colchester on Marks Tey to Sudbury branch
Length of Line: A third of a mile

Nº of Steam Locos: 5   **Other Locos:** 4
Nº of Members: 750
Annual Membership Fee: Adult £20.00; Senior Citizen £15.00
Approx Nº of Visitors P.A.: 40,000
Gauge: Standard
Web site: www.earm.co.uk

GENERAL INFORMATION

Nearest Mainline Station: Chappel & Wakes Colne (adajcent)
Nearest Bus Stop: Wakes Colne Post Office (400 yards)
Car Parking: Free parking at site
Coach Parking: Free parking at site
Souvenir Shop(s): Yes
Food & Drinks: Snacks and drinks are available

SPECIAL INFORMATION

The museum has the most comprehensive collection of railway architecture & engineering in the region. The railway also has a miniature railway that usually operates on steam days.

OPERATING INFORMATION

Opening Times: Open daily 12.00pm to 4.30pm. Steam days open from 12.30pm to 4.30pm. Closed on Christmas Day and Boxing Day.
Steam Working: Steam days are held every month from April to September and also in October and December. Bank Holidays are also Steam days. Check the web site for further details.
Prices: Adult £6.00 static viewing; £9.00 Steam
Child £3.00 static viewing; £4.50 Steam
O.A.P. £5.00 static viewing; £8.00 Steam
Children under the age of 4 are admitted free of charge. A 10% discount is available for bookings for more than 10 people. A 10% discount is also available for visitors who visit using Mainline trains!

Detailed Directions by Car:
From North & South: Turn off the A12 south west of Colchester onto the A1124 (formerly the A604). The Museum is situated just off the A1124; From West: Turn off the A120 just before Marks Tey (signposted).

EAST KENT RAILWAY

Address: Station Road, Shepherdswell, Dover, Kent CT15 7PD	**Nº of Steam Locos:** None at present
Telephone Nº: (01304) 832042	**Nº of Other Locos:** 4 + 3 DMUs
Year Formed: 1985	**Nº of Members:** 250
Location of Line: Between Shepherdswell and Eythorne	**Annual Membership Fee:** £15.00 (Adult)
Length of Line: 2 miles	**Approx Nº of Visitors P.A.:** 15,500
	Gauge: Standard gauge and also 5 inch and 7¼ inch miniature gauges
	Web site: www.eastkentrailway.co.uk

GENERAL INFORMATION

Nearest Mainline Station: Shepherdswell (50 yards)
Car Parking: Available Shepherdswell and Eythorne
Coach Parking: Available at both stations by prior arrangement.
Souvenir Shop(s): Yes
Food & Drinks: Yes – both hot and cold available

SPECIAL INFORMATION

The East Kent Railway was originally built between 1911 and 1917 to service Tilmanstone Colliery. Closed in the mid-1980's, the railway was re-opened in 1995.

OPERATING INFORMATION

Opening Times: The 2017 operating season runs from 1st April until 24th September. Trains operate every Sunday and Bank Holiday during this period plus Saturdays in July and August and during some other special events including Halloween and Santa Specials. Please contact the railway for details about group bookings: party@eastkentrailway.co.uk
Steam Working: None at present.
Prices: Adult £6.00   Child £3.00
          Senior Citizens £5.00
          Family £15.00 (2 Adults and 2 Children)

Detailed Directions by Car:
From the A2: Take the turning to Shepherdswell and continue to the village. Pass the shop on the left and cross the railway bridge. Take the next left (Station Road) signposted at the traffic lights for the EKR; From the A256: Take the turning for Eythorne at the roundabout on the section between Eastry and Whitfield. Follow the road through Eythorne. Further on you will cross the railway line and enter Shepherdswell. After a few hundred yards take the right turn signposted for the EKR.

EAST LANCASHIRE RAILWAY

Address: Bolton Street Station, Bury, Lancashire BL9 0EY **Telephone N°:** (0161) 764-7790 **Year Formed:** 1968 **Location of Line:** Heywood, Bury and Rawtenstall **Length of Line:** 12 miles	**N° of Steam Locos:** 14 **N° of Other Locos:** 37 **N° of Members:** 3,500 **Annual Membership Fee:** £19.00 **Approx N° of Visitors P.A.:** 163,000 **Gauge:** Standard **Web site:** www.eastlancsrailway.org.uk

GENERAL INFORMATION

Nearest Mainline Station: Manchester (then Metrolink to Bury)
Nearest Bus Station: ¼ mile
Car Parking: Adjacent
Coach Parking: Adjacent
Souvenir Shop(s): Yes
Food & Drinks: Yes

SPECIAL INFORMATION

Originally opened in 1846, the East Lancashire Railway was re-opened in 1987.

OPERATING INFORMATION

Opening Times: Every weekend & Bank Holiday 9.00am to 5.00pm. Also Wednesday to Friday from 1st April to 30th September 2017. A number of special events (including Santa Specials) run during the year. Please contact the railway for details.
Steam Working: Most trains are steam-hauled. Saturdays alternate Steam & Diesel. Two engines are in steam on Sundays.
Prices: Adult Return £8.20 – £14.80
Child Return £5.20 – £9.40
Concessionary Return £7.40 – £13.30
Family Return £38.00
Cheaper fares are available for shorter journeys.

Detailed Directions by Car:
From All Parts: Exit the M66 at Junction 2 and take the A56 into Bury. Follow the brown tourist signs and turn right into Bolton Street at the junction with the A58. The station is about 150 yards on the right.

EAST SOMERSET RAILWAY

Address: Cranmore Railway Station, Shepton Mallet, Somerset BA4 4QP	**Nº of Steam Locos:** 5
Telephone Nº: (01749) 880417	**Nº of Other Locos:** 5
Year Formed: 1971	**Nº of Members:** 480
Location of Line: Cranmore, off A361 between Frome and Shepton Mallet	**Annual Membership Fee:** £19.00 (Adult)
	Approx Nº of Visitors P.A.: 20,000
Length of Line: 3 miles	**Gauge:** Standard
	Web site: www.eastsomersetrailway.com

GENERAL INFORMATION

Nearest Mainline Station: Castle Cary (10 miles)
Nearest Bus Station: Shepton Mallet (3 miles)
Car Parking: Space for 100 cars available
Coach Parking: Yes
Souvenir Shop(s): Yes
Food & Drinks: Yes

SPECIAL INFORMATION

Footplate experience courses available – phone (01749) 880417 for further details.

E-mail: info@eastsomersetrailway.com

OPERATING INFORMATION

Opening Times: Complex, Museum and Engine Sheds open daily from April to December and Tuesdays, Thursdays, Saturdays, January to March. Closed on Mondays and Wednesdays in November.
Steam Working: 2017 dates: Weekends and Bank Holidays from 18th March to 29th October, Wednesdays from 7th June to 11th October and Thursdays from 27th July to 31st August.
Santa Specials run on some December weekends. Special events on other dates. Open 10.00am to 4.00pm (5.30pm in the Summer).
Day Rover Ticket Prices: Adult £9.00 Child £7.00 Senior Citizen £8.00 Family £28.00

Detailed Directions by Car:
From the North: Take A367/A37 to Shepton Mallet then turn left onto A361 to Frome. Carry on to Shepton Mallet and 9 miles after Frome turn left at Cranmore; From the South: Take A36 to Frome bypass then A361 to Cranmore; From the West: Take A371 from Wells to Shepton Mallet, then A361 to Frome (then as above).

ECCLESBOURNE VALLEY RAILWAY

Address: Station Road, Coldwell Street, Wirksworth DE4 4FB **Telephone Nº**: (01629) 823076 **Year Formed**: 2000 **Location of Line**: Ravenstor to Duffield **Length of Line**: 8½ miles	**Nº of Steam Locos**: 4 (2 operational) **Nº of Other Locos**: 12 (including DMUs) **Nº of Members**: 700+ **Annual Membership Fee**: £15.00 **Approx Nº of Visitors P.A.**: 25,000 **Gauge**: Standard **Web site**: www.e-v-r.com

GENERAL INFORMATION

Nearest Mainline Station: Duffield (adjacent)
Nearest Bus Station: Derby (13 miles)
Car Parking: Available at the Station
Coach Parking: Available at Wirksworth Station
Souvenir Shop(s): Yes
Food & Drinks: Yes

SPECIAL INFORMATION

The line was restored section by section and the Railway opened all 8½ miles in April 2011.

OPERATING INFORMATION

Opening Times: 2017 dates: Weekends and Bank Holidays from 11th February until 29th October. Also open on Saturdays in November, Tuesdays from 14th February until 28th November, Thursdays from 1st June until 28th September (as well as during the Easter Holidays and half terms) and Fridays from 7th July to 1st September. Timetables vary depending on the date. Please contact the railway for further details.
Steam Working: Weekends and Bank Holidays from 27th May to 28th August (but closed on 12th, 13th, 19th & 20th August).
Prices: Adult Day Rover £13.00
Child Day Rover £6.50
Concessions Day Rover £12.00
Family Day Rover £33.00
Note: Prices vary depending on journey length.

Detailed Directions by Car:
From All Parts: Exit the M1 at Junction 26 and take the A610 Ambergate then the A6 to Whatstandwell. Turn left onto the B5035 to Wirksworth and the station is at the bottom of the hill as you enter the town.

ELSECAR HERITAGE RAILWAY   (COALFIELD LINE)

Address: Wath Road, Elsecar, Barnsley, S74 8HJ
Telephone Nº: (01226) 746746
Year Formed: 1997
Location of Line: Elsecar, near Barnsley
Length of Line: 1 mile (due to increase to 2 miles during 2017)

Nº of Steam Locos: 4
Nº of Other Locos: 3
Nº of Members: Approximately 160
Annual Membership Fee: £15.00
Approx Nº of Visitors P.A.: 30,000
Gauge: Standard
Web site: www.elsecarrailway.co.uk

GENERAL INFORMATION

Nearest Mainline Station: Elsecar
Nearest Bus Station: Barnsley
Car Parking: Large free car park at the site
Coach Parking: At the site, by arrangement only
Souvenir Shop(s): Yes
Food & Drinks: Yes

SPECIAL INFORMATION

The Railway is based at the Elsecar Heritage Centre which is an antiques and craft centre with a wide range of displays and special events.

OPERATING INFORMATION

Opening Times: The Heritage Centre is open daily from 10.00am to 4.00pm (closed from 25th December to 2nd January). Trains run on most Sundays and Bank Holidays throughout the year. Also open on most Mondays and Wednesdays for static viewing. Hourly services operate from 12.00pm to 2.00pm.
Steam Working: Most services are steam-hauled. Please phone for further information.
Prices: Adults £5.00   Children £2.50
Senior Citizens £4.00
Admission to the site is free of charge except for during Special Events.

Detailed Directions by Car:

From All Parts: Exit the M1 at Junction 36 and follow the brown 'Elsecar Heritage' signs taking the A6135 for approximately 2 miles. Turn left onto Broad Carr Road for just under a mile, then right onto Armroyd Lane and right again onto Fitzwilliam Street. Free visitor car parking is available on Wentworth Road off the junction of Fitzwilliam Street and Wath Road.

EMBSAY & BOLTON ABBEY STEAM RAILWAY

Address: Bolton Abbey Station, Bolton Abbey, Skipton, N. Yorkshire BD23 6AF	**Nº of Steam Locos**: 14
Telephone Nº: (01756) 710614	**Nº of Other Locos**: 12
Year Formed: 1968	**Nº of Members**: 800
Location of Line: 2 miles east of Skipton	**Annual Membership Fee**: £20.00
Length of Line: 4½ miles	**Approx Nº of Visitors P.A.**: 110,000
	Gauge: Standard

GENERAL INFORMATION

Nearest Mainline Station: Skipton (2 miles), Ilkley (3 miles)
Nearest Bus Station: Skipton (2 miles), Ilkley (3 mls)
Car Parking: Large car park at both Stations
Coach Parking: Large coach park at both Stations
Souvenir Shop(s): Yes
Food & Drinks: Yes – Cafe + Buffet cars

SPECIAL INFORMATION

The line extension to Bolton Abbey opened in 1998.

Web site: www.embsayboltonabbeyrailway.org.uk

OPERATING INFORMATION

Opening Times: Every Sunday throughout the year. Weekends from April to the end of October and daily in the summer season until early September. Tuesdays from April to October and also on a number of other dates. Santa Specials run on December weekends. Contact the railway for details.
Steam Working: Steam trains depart Embsay Station at 10.30am, 12.00pm, 1.30pm, 3.00pm and 4.30pm on most days during the Main Season. Contact the railway for further details.
Prices: Adult Return £11.00   Child Return £5.50
Concessionary Return £10.00
Family Ticket £27.50 (2 adult + 2 children)
Different fares may apply on special event days.

Detailed Directions by Car:
From All Parts: Embsay Station is off the A59 Skipton bypass by the Harrogate Road. Bolton Abbey Station is off the A59 at Bolton Abbey.

EPPING ONGAR RAILWAY

Address: Ongar Station, Ongar, Essex, CM5 9BN	**N° of Steam Locos:** 3
Telephone N°: (01277) 365200	**N° of Other Locos:** 7
Year Formed: 2004	**N° of Members:** 600
Location of Line: Epping Forest to Ongar	**Approx N° of Visitors P.A.:** 40,000
Length of Line: 6.3 miles	**Gauge:** Standard gauge
	Web site: www.eorailway.co.uk

GENERAL INFORMATION

Nearest Mainline Station: Epping Underground – Central line (7½ miles to Ongar Station)
Nearest Bus Station: Epping (7½ miles)
Car Parking: Limited free parking at Ongar Station and plenty of spaces at Epping Station. There is no parking whatsoever at North Weald Station.
Coach Parking: By arrangement only
Souvenir Shop(s): Yes
Food & Drinks: Available at Ongar and North Weald

SPECIAL INFORMATION

A frequent heritage bus service (number 339) runs from Epping Tube Station (and Shenfield Train Station during the summer) to the railway every operating day. A further bus service (number 381) runs from Epping to North Weald on selected dates.

OPERATING INFORMATION

Opening Times: 2017 dates: Weekends and Bank Holidays from 1st April to 29th October and for Santa Specials during December. Also open on Wednesdays during the summer school holidays.
Steam Working: Most operating days.
Prices: Adults £13.00
Children £7.00
Senior Citizens £11.00
Family Ticket £34.00

Detailed Directions by Car:
For North Weald Station: Exit the M11 at Junction 7 and follow the A414 towards Chelmsford and North Weald. Take the 3rd exit at the 2nd roundabout ('The Talbot' pub on the left) and follow the road into North Weald village. Station Road is on the left just after leaving the village. For Ongar Station: Exit the M11 at Junction 7 and follow the A414 towards Chelmsford and North Weald. Follow the road for approximately 5 miles going straight on at two roundabouts. At the 3rd roundabout (BP garage on the left) take the third exit towards Ongar. Epping Ongar Railway is located on the right hand side after approximately 400 yards.

FOXFIELD STEAM RAILWAY

Address: Caverswall Road Station, Blythe Bridge, Stoke-on-Trent, Staffs. ST11 9EA
Telephone Nº: (01782) 396210
Year Formed: 1967
Location of Line: Blythe Bridge
Length of Line: 3½ miles
Gauge: Standard and 7¼ inch miniature

Nº of Steam Locos: 20
Nº of Other Locos: 12
Nº of Members: Over 300
Annual Membership Fee: Adult £12.00; Junior £6.00; Family £20.00
Approx Nº of Visitors P.A.: 25,000
Web site: www.foxfieldrailway.co.uk

GENERAL INFORMATION

Nearest Mainline Station: Blythe Bridge (¼ mile)
Nearest Bus Station: Hanley (5 miles)
Car Parking: Space for 300 cars available
Coach Parking: Space for 6 coaches available
Souvenir Shop(s): Yes
Food & Drinks: Yes – Buffet and Real Ale Bar

SPECIAL INFORMATION

The Railway is a former Colliery railway built in 1893 to take coal from Foxfield Colliery. It has the steepest Standard Gauge adhesion worked gradient in the UK and freight trains can be seen on these gradients during the annual Steam Gala in July.

OPERATING INFORMATION

Opening Times: 2017 dates: Sundays & Bank Holiday Mondays from 26th March to 29th October. Also Wednesdays from 26th July to 30th August and weekends from 25th November to 24th December. Open 11.00am to 5.00pm.
Steam Working: Usually 11.30am, 1.00pm, 2.30pm and 4.00pm although Special Event days may run trains at different times.
Prices: Adult Ticket £8.00
    Child Ticket £3.50 (3-16 years old)
    Senior Citizen Ticket £6.50
    Family Ticket £21.00 (2 adult + 2 children)
Note: Fares for Special Events may vary.

Detailed Directions by Car:
From South: Exit M6 at Junction 14 onto the A34 to Stone then the A520 to Meir and the A50 to Blythe Bridge; From North: Exit M6 at Junction 15 then the A500 to Stoke-on-Trent and the A50 to Blythe Bridge; From East: Take the A50 to Blythe Bridge. Once in Blythe Bridge, turn by the Mainline crossing.

GLOUCESTERSHIRE WARWICKSHIRE RAILWAY

Address: The Station, Toddington, Cheltenham, Gloucestershire GL54 5DT	**Nº of Steam Locos**: 7
Telephone Nº: (01242) 621405	**Nº of Other Locos**: 17
Year Formed: 1981	**Nº of Members**: 4,250
Location of Line: 5 miles south of Broadway, Worcestershire, near the A46	**Annual Membership Fee**: £20.00 (Adult)
Length of Line: 12 miles	**Approx Nº of Visitors P.A.**: 100,000
	Gauge: Standard and Narrow gauge
	Web site: www.gwsr.com

GENERAL INFORMATION

Nearest Mainline Station: Cheltenham Spa, Ashchurch or Evesham
Nearest Bus Station: Cheltenham
Car Parking: Parking available at Toddington and Cheltenham Racecourse Stations
Coach Parking: As above, by prior arrangement
Souvenir Shop(s): Yes   **Food & Drinks**: Yes

SPECIAL INFORMATION

The railway has so far restored and reopened 12 miles of line and is in the process of raising £1.5 million to extend the track 3 miles northwards to Broadway. The ultimate aim is to extend a further 6 miles to Honeybourne in the future.

OPERATING INFORMATION

Opening Times: The railway is operational for 169 days during 2017, mainly on weekends plus Tuesdays, Wednesdays and Thursdays. Please check the web site for further information. The first train leaves at 10.00am.
Steam Working: Weekends from March to October and various other dates.
Prices: Adult Day Rover £17.00
Child Day Rover £7.00
Senior Citizen Day Rover £16.00
Family Ticket Day Rover £44.00
(2 Adults + 3 Children)
Under 5's travel free of charge apart from on some Special Event days.

Detailed Directions by Car:
Toddington is 11 miles north east of Cheltenham, 5 miles south of Broadway just off the B4632 (old A46). Exit the M5 at Junction 9 towards Stow-on-the-Wold for the B4632. The Railway is clearly visible from the B4632.

GREAT CENTRAL RAILWAY

Address: Great Central Station, Great Central Road, Loughborough, Leicestershire LE11 1RW **Telephone N°**: (01509) 632323 **Year Formed**: 1969 **Location of Line**: From Loughborough to Leicester	**Length of Line**: 8 miles **N° of Steam Locos**: 10 **N° of Other Locos**: 11 **N° of Members**: 5,000 **Annual Membership Fee**: £24.00 **Approx N° of Visitors P.A.**: 125,000 **Gauge**: Standard

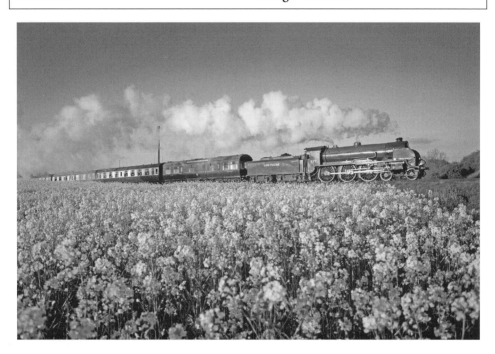

GENERAL INFORMATION

Nearest Mainline Station: Loughborough (1 mile)
Nearest Bus Station: Loughborough (½ mile)
Car Parking: Street parking outside the Station
Coach Parking: Car parks at Quorn & Woodhouse, Rothley and Leicester North
Souvenir Shop(s): Yes
Food & Drinks: Yes – Buffet or Restaurant cars are usually available for snacks or other meals

Web site: www.gcrailway.co.uk

SPECIAL INFORMATION

The aim of the GCR is to recreate the experience of British main line railway operation during the best years of steam locomotives.

OPERATING INFORMATION

Opening Times: 2017 dates: Weekends throughout the year, Wednesdays from June to October and Tuesdays and Thursdays over the summer holidays. Santa Specials in December and other dates throughout the year. Contact the railway for details.
Steam Working: Weekends, Bank Holidays and some Special Events throughout the year.
Prices: Adult Day ticket £16.00
　　　　　Child Day ticket £9.00
　　　　　Senior Citizen Day ticket £14.00
　　　　　Family Day Ticket £35 (2 adults + 3 children)

Detailed Directions by Car:
Great Central Road is on the South East side of Loughborough and is clearly signposted from the A6 Leicester Road and A60 Nottingham Road.

GREAT CENTRAL RAILWAY (NOTTINGHAM)

Address: Nottingham Transport Heritage Centre, Mere Way, Ruddington, Nottingham   NG11 6NX
Telephone Nº: (0115) 940-5705
Fax Nº: (0115) 940-5905
Year Formed: 1990 (Opened in 1994)
Location of Line: Ruddington to Loughborough Junction

Length of Line: 9 miles
Nº of Steam Locos: 6
Nº of Other Locos: 10
Nº of Members: 750
Annual Membership Fee: £14.00
Approx Nº of Visitors P.A.: 15,000
Gauge: Standard
Web site: www.gcrn.co.uk

GENERAL INFORMATION

Nearest Mainline Station: Nottingham (5 miles)
Nearest Bus Station: Bus service from Nottingham to Ruddington
Car Parking: Available on site (£2.00 charge)
Coach Parking: Free parking at site
Souvenir Shop(s): Yes   **Food & Drinks:** Yes

SPECIAL INFORMATION

The Heritage Centre covers an area of more than eleven acres and is set within the Rushcliffe Country Park in Ruddington. All trains run to Loughborough Junction.

OPERATING INFORMATION

Opening Times: 2017 dates: Sundays and Bank Holidays plus some Saturdays from 1st April until 29th October. Open 10.45am to 5.00pm. Also open for Santa Specials on 26th November and weekends in December.
Steam Working: Steam service runs from 11.00am
Prices: Adult £12.00
Child £6.00 (Ages 5 to 15)
Family £30.00 (2 adults + 3 children)
Note: Prices shown above are for unlimited day rover tickets.

Detailed Directions by Car:
From All Parts: The centre is situated off the A60 Nottingham to Loughborough Road and is signposted just south of the traffic lights at Ruddington.

GWILI RAILWAY

Address: Bronwydd Arms Station, Bronwydd Arms, Carmarthen SA33 6HT	**Nº of Steam Locos:** 3
Telephone Nº: (01267) 238213	**Nº of Other Locos:** 3
E-mail: jjohn@gwili-railway.co.uk	**Nº of Members:** 900 shareholders, 380 Society members
Year Formed: 1975	**Annual Membership Fee:** £18.00 (Adult)
Location of Line: Near Carmarthen, South Wales	**Approx Nº of Visitors P.A.:** 28,000
Length of Line: 2½ miles at present	**Gauge:** Standard
	Web site: www.gwili-railway.co.uk

GENERAL INFORMATION

Nearest Mainline Station: Carmarthen (3 miles)
Nearest Bus Station: Carmarthen (3 miles)
Car Parking: Free parking at Bronwydd Arms
Coach Parking: Free parking at Bronwydd Arms
Souvenir Shop(s): Yes
Food & Drinks: Yes

SPECIAL INFORMATION

Gwili Railway was the first Standard Gauge preserved railway in West Wales. There is a riverside picnic area and Miniature railway at Llwyfan Cerrig Station and there is a Signal Box Museum at Bronwydd Arms. The railway plans to extend the line to Abergwili Junction in the future.

OPERATING INFORMATION

Opening Times: 2017 dates: Open every weekend plus Wednesdays and Thursdays from 8th April to 31st October. Also open daily in July and August. Santa Specials on operate on December weekends. Please contact the railway for details about Special Event days.

Steam Working: All advertised trains are steam hauled. Trains run from 11.00am to 3.00pm.

Prices: Adult £11.00
Child £5.00 (Under-2s ride free of charge)
Family £27.50 (2 adults + up to 2 children)
Senior Citizens £10.00

Note: Discounts are available for larger groups (20+).

Detailed Directions by Car:
The Railway is three miles North of Carmarthen – signposted off the A484 Carmarthen to Cardigan Road.

HEAD OF STEAM – DARLINGTON RAILWAY MUSEUM

Address: North Road Station, Darlington, Co. Durham DL3 6ST
Telephone Nº: (01325) 405060
Year Formed: 1975
Location of Line: Adjacent to North Road Station
Length of Line: ¼ mile

Nº of Steam Locos: 4
Nº of Other Locos: None
Nº of Members: 800 family memberships
Annual Membership Fee: £10.00 (adult) £15.00 (family); £10.00 (senior)
Approx Nº of Visitors P.A.: 33,500
Gauge: Standard
Web site: www.head-of-steam.co.uk

GENERAL INFORMATION

Nearest Mainline Station: North Road (adjacent)
Nearest Bus Station: Darlington (1 mile)
Car Parking: Free parking at site
Coach Parking: Free parking at site
Souvenir Shop(s): Yes
Food & Drinks: Refreshments are available from the reception.

SPECIAL INFORMATION

The museum is an 1842 station on the route of the Stockton and Darlington Railway and is devoted to the Railways of north-east England.

OPERATING INFORMATION

Opening Times: The Museum is open daily throughout the year but is closed every Monday. from April to September and every Monday and Tuesday from October to March. Also closed on Christmas Day, Boxing Day and New Year's Day. Open 10.00am to 4.00pm April to September and from 11.00am to 3.30pm from October to March.
Steam Working: None planned for 2017.
Prices: Adult £4.95
Child £3.00 (ages 5 and under enter free)
Senior Citizen £3.75
Family Ticket £10.00
                    (2 adults and up to 3 children)

Detailed Directions by Car:
From Darlington Town Centre: Follow the A167 north for about ¾ mile then turn left immediately before the Railway bridge; From A1(M): Exit at Junction 59 then follow A167 towards Darlington and turn right after passing under the Railway bridge.

HELSTON RAILWAY

Address: Trevarno Farm, Prospidnick, Helston, Cornwall TR13 0RY	**Nº of Steam Locos**: None at present
Contact Telephone Nº: 07901 977597	**Nº of Other Locos**: 2 (plus 1 DMU)
E-mail: info@helstonrailway.co.uk	**Nº of Members**: 1,000 approximately
Year Formed: 2002	**Annual Membership Fee**: £15.00
Location: Trevarno Farm, Helston	**Approx Nº of Visitors P.A.**: 4,500
Length of Line: 1 mile	**Gauge**: Standard
	Web site: www.helstonrailway.co.uk

GENERAL INFORMATION

Nearest Mainline Station: Camborne (6 miles)
Nearest Bus Station: Camborne
Car Parking: Free parking at Trevano Farm
Coach Parking: At Trevano Farm
Souvenir Shop(s): Yes
Food & Drinks: Light refreshments are available

SPECIAL INFORMATION

The Helston Railway was formed in 2002 and has reinstated a 1 mile section of track which is open for rides. The long term aim is to reopen a 3 mile section of the line to reach the outskirts of Helston Water-ma-Trout.

OPERATING INFORMATION

Opening Times: Every Thursday, Sunday and Bank Holiday Mondays from Easter to November. Open from 10.30am to 4.00pm and also for some Evening Specials during the summer months.
Steam Working: Rushton Diesel and Brake Van rides only at present but the railway hopes to have visiting steam locos in the future.
Prices: Adults £7.00 (Brake Van rides)
Children £4.00 (Brake Van rides)
(Under-5s ride free of charge)
Family Ticket £15.00 (2 adults + 3 children)
Shunter Footplate Rides £10.00 (Adults)
Note: Access to the railway is via Trevarno Farm car park where free parking is available.

Detailed Directions by Car:
The railway is situated 1½ miles to the north of Helston, just off the B3303 between Crowntown and Nancegollan.

ISLE OF WIGHT STEAM RAILWAY

Address: The Railway Station, Havenstreet, Near Ryde, Isle of Wight PO33 4DS
Telephone Nº: (01983) 882204
Year Formed: 1971 (re-opened)
Location: Smallbrook Junction to Wootton
Length of Line: 5 miles
Nº of Steam Locos: 12

Nº of Other Locos: 3
Nº of Members: Over 1,000
Annual Membership Fee: £25.00 (Adult)
Approx Nº of Visitors P.A.: 110,000
Gauge: Standard
Talking Timetable: (01983) 884343
Web site: www.iwsteamrailway.co.uk

GENERAL INFORMATION

Nearest Mainline Station: Smallbrook Junction (direct interchange)
Nearest Bus: From Ryde & Newport direct
Car Parking: Free parking at Havenstreet & Wootton Stations
Coach Parking: Free at Havenstreet Station
Souvenir Shop(s): Yes – at Havenstreet Station
Food & Drinks: Yes – at Havenstreet Station

SPECIAL INFORMATION

The IWSR uses mostly Victorian & Edwardian locomotives and carriages to recreate the atmosphere of an Isle of Wight branch line railway.

OPERATING INFORMATION

Opening Times: 2017 dates: Most days in April, May, June and September and daily from 24th June to 15th September. Open on Wednesdays, Thursdays and Sundays in October plus Santa Specials on weekends and other dates in December.
Please contact the railway for further information.
Steam Working: 10.05am to 4.20pm (depending on the Station and also the time of year)
Prices: Adult Day Ticket £11.50 – £20.00
            Child Day Ticket £6.00 – £13.50
                        (Under-5s travel free)
            Family Day Ticket £29.00 – £53.50
                        (2 adults + 2 children)
Note: Discounted prices are available for online bookings and First Class tickets are also available.

Detailed Directions by Car:
To reach the Isle of Wight head for the Ferry ports at Lymington, Southampton or Portsmouth. From all parts of the Isle of Wight, head for Havenstreet (which is located 3 miles from Ryde and 3 miles from Newport), and follow the brown tourist signs.

KEIGHLEY & WORTH VALLEY RAILWAY

Address: The Station, Haworth, Keighley, West Yorkshire BD22 8NJ
Telephone Nº: (01535) 645214 (enquiries)
Year Formed: 1962 (Line re-opened 1968)
Location of Line: From Keighley southwards through Haworth to Oxenhope
Length of Line: 4¾ miles

Nº of Steam Locos: 30   **Other Locos:** 10
Members: 5,000 (350 working members)
Annual Membership Fee: Adult £25.00; Adult life membership £491.00
Approx Nº of Visitors P.A.: 120,000
Gauge: Standard
Web Site: www.kwvr.co.uk

GENERAL INFORMATION

Nearest Mainline Station: Keighley (adjacent)
Nearest Bus Station: Keighley (5 minutes walk)
Car Parking: Parking at Keighley, Ingrow, Haworth (charged) and Oxenhope
Coach Parking: At Ingrow & Oxenhope (phone in advance)
Souvenir Shop(s): Yes – at Keighley, Oxenhope & Haworth (whose shop also sells books/DVDs)
Food & Drinks: Yes – at Keighley & Oxenhope when trains run.

SPECIAL INFORMATION

There are two award-winning Railway Museums adjacent to the Ingrow Station.

OPERATING INFORMATION

Opening Times: 2017 dates: Weekends & Bank Holidays throughout the year. Daily from 27th May to 10th September. Also open during the Easter, Whit, February and October School holidays and daily from 26th December to 1st Janury 2018.
Steam Working: Early trains are Diesel; Steam runs from mid-morning on all operating days including the 4 weekends prior to Christmas when Santa Specials operate (pre-booking necessary for these).
Prices: Adult Return £11.00   (£16.00 Day Rover)
Child Return £5.60   (£8.00 Day Rover)
Family Day Rover £40.00 (2 adult + 3 child)
Small Family Day Rover £20.00 (1 + 1 child)
Concession Day Rover £14.00
Concession Return £10.00

Detailed Directions by Car:
Exit the M62 at Junction 26 and take the M606 to its' end. Follow the ring-road signs around Bradford to Shipley. Take the A650 through Bingley to Keighley and follow the brown tourist signs to the railway. Alternatively, take the A6033 from Hebden Bridge to Oxenhope and follow the brown signs to Oxenhope or Haworth Stations.

THE KEITH & DUFFTOWN RAILWAY

Address: Dufftown Station, Dufftown, Banffshire, AB55 4BA **Telephone Nº**: (01340) 821181 **Year Formed**: 2000 **Location of Line**: Keith to Dufftown **Length of Line**: 11 miles	**Nº of Steam Locos**: None at present **Nº of Other Locos**: 6 DMU + 3 shunters **Nº of Members**: Approximately 400 **Annual Membership Fee**: Adult £15.00 **Approx Nº of Visitors P.A.**: Not known **Gauge**: Standard **Web**: www.keith-dufftown-railway.co.uk

GENERAL INFORMATION

Nearest Mainline Station: Keith (½ mile)
Nearest Bus Station: Elgin (Bus routes travel to both Keith and Dufftown)
Car Parking: Available at both Stations
Coach Parking: Available at both Stations
Souvenir Shop(s): Yes – at Keith Town Station
Food & Drinks: Available at Dufftown Station

SPECIAL INFORMATION

The Keith and Dufftown Railway is an eleven mile line linking the World's Malt Whisky Capital, Dufftown, to the market town of Keith. The line, which was reopened by volunteers during 2000 and 2001, passes through some of Scotland's most picturesque scenery, with forest and farmland, lochs and glens, castles and distilleries.

OPERATING INFORMATION

Opening Times: Weekends from Easter until the end of September and also on Fridays from June, to September inclusive. Trains depart Dufftown from 11.10am until 4.00pm.
Steam Working: None at present
Prices: Adult Return £11.00
Child Return £5.00
Concessionary Return £9.00
Family Return £28.00
Note: Shorter journeys are cheaper.

Detailed Directions by Car:
Keith Town Station is located in Keith, on the A96 Aberdeen to Inverness Road; Dufftown Station is about 1 mile to the north of the Dufftown Town Centre just off the A941 road to Elgin.

KENT & EAST SUSSEX RAILWAY

Address: Tenterden Town Station, Tenterden, Kent TN30 6HE	**No of Steam Locos**: 12
Telephone No: (01580) 765155	**No of Other Locos**: 6
Year Formed: 1974	**No of Members**: 2,100
Location of Line: Tenterden, Kent to Bodiam, East Sussex	**Annual Membership Fee**: £25.00 (Adult)
	Approx No of Visitors P.A.: 99,000
	Gauge: Standard
Length of Line: 10½ miles	**Web site**: www.kesr.org.uk

GENERAL INFORMATION

Nearest Mainline Station: Headcorn (8 miles)
Nearest Bus Station: Tenterden
Car Parking: Free parking available at Tenterden Town and Northiam Stations
Coach Parking: Tenterden & Northiam
Souvenir Shop(s): Yes
Food & Drinks: Yes

SPECIAL INFORMATION

Built as Britain's first light railway, the K&ESR opened in 1900 and was epitomised by sharp curved and steep gradients and to this day retains a charm and atmosphere all of its own.

OPERATING INFORMATION

Opening Times: 2017 dates: Weekends and Bank Holidays from 1st April to 29th October and also in December (but closed on 30th & 31st December). Tuesday to Thursday in May, June, July and September and daily during August. Also open on other dates. Please contact the railway for details. Trains depart from 10.40am. Phone (01580) 762943 for the 24 hour talking-timetable.
Steam Working: Every operational day
Prices: Adult Ticket – £18.00
            Child Ticket – £12.00
            Family Ticket – £38.00
            (2 adults + 3 children or 1 adult + 4 children)
Note: Prices shown are for All Day travel tickets. Advance purchases are cheaper. First Class upgrades are available for £2.00 (Family ticket upgrade £6.50)

Detailed Directions by Car:
From London and Kent Coast: Travel to Ashford (M20) then take the A28 to Tenterden; From Sussex Coast: Take A28 from Hastings to Northiam.

LAKESIDE & HAVERTHWAITE RAILWAY

Address: Haverthwaite Station, near Ulverston, Cumbria LA12 8AL	**Length of Line:** 3½ miles
Telephone Nº: (015395) 31594	**Nº of Steam Locos:** 7
E-mail: info@lakesiderailway.co.uk	**Nº of Other Locos:** 6
Year Formed: 1973	**Approx Nº of Visitors P.A.:** 170,000
Location of Line: Haverthwaite to Lakeside	**Gauge:** Standard
	Web site: www.lakesiderailway.co.uk

GENERAL INFORMATION

Nearest Mainline Station: Ulverston (7 miles)
Nearest Bus Station: Haverthwaite (100 yards)
Car Parking: Plenty of spaces – Charges from £1.00
Coach Parking: Free parking at site
Souvenir Shop(s): Yes
Food & Drinks: Yes

SPECIAL INFORMATION

Tickets which include train ride followed by a cruise on Lake Windermere or a visit to the Aquarium of the Lakes are also available from the Railway.

OPERATING INFORMATION

Opening Times: 2017 dates: Daily from 1st April to 29th October inclusive. A Diesel-only service operates from 30th October to 5th November. Also open for Santa Specials during weekends from 2nd to 17th December. A number of other Special Events run throughout the year. Please contact the railway for further information.
Steam Working: Daily unless otherwise advertised
Prices: Adult Return £6.80   Single £4.20
        Adult Day Rover £10.00
        Child Return £3.40   Single £2.70
        Child Day Rover £5.00
        Family Ticket £19.50 (2 adult + 3 child)
Note: Prices vary for Special Events and individual fares apply for combined tickets including other attractions.

Detailed Directions by Car:
From All Parts: Exit the M6 at Junction 36 and follow the brown tourist signs.

THE LAVENDER LINE

Address: Isfield Station, Isfield, near Uckfield, East Sussex TN22 5XB
Telephone Nº: (01825) 750515
Year Formed: 1992
Location of Line: East Sussex between Lewes and Uckfield
Length of Line: 1 mile

Nº of Steam Locos: 3 (1 in service)
Nº of Other Locos: 4 + DEMU
Nº of Members: Approximately 400
Annual Membership Fee: £15.00
Approx Nº of Visitors P.A.: 12,500
Gauge: Standard
Web site: www.lavender-line.co.uk

GENERAL INFORMATION

Nearest Mainline Station: Uckfield (3 miles)
Nearest Bus Station: Uckfield (3 miles)
Car Parking: Free parking on site
Coach Parking: Can cater for coach parties – please contact the Railway.
Souvenir Shop: Yes
Food & Drinks: Yes – Cinders Buffet

SPECIAL INFORMATION

Isfield Station has been restored as a Southern Railway country station complete with the original London Brighton & South Coast Railway signal box.

OPERATING INFORMATION

Opening Times: Sundays and Bank Holidays throughout the year plus a number of other Special Event dates including Summer Specials on Thursdays and Fridays in August and Santa Specials in December. Please contact the railway for further details.
Steam Working: Generally, the first and last Sunday of the month April to October inclusive plus some other dates. Contact the railway for further details.
Prices: Adult £9.00
Child £6.00
Senior Citizen £7.00
Family Ticket £28.00 (2 adults + 3 children)
All tickets offer unlimited rides on the day of issue and prices may vary on special event days.

Detailed Directions by Car::
From All Parts: Isfield is just off the A26 midway between Lewes and Uckfield.

LINCOLNSHIRE WOLDS RAILWAY

Address: The Railway Station, Ludborough, Lincolnshire   DN36 5SQ
Telephone Nº: (01507) 363881
Year Formed: 1979
Location of Line: Ludborough – off the A16(T) between Grimsby and Louth
Length of Line: 1½ miles

Nº of Steam Locos: 5   **Other Locos**: 7
Nº of Members: 400+
Annual Membership Fee: £36.00 Family, £18.00 Adult, £12.00 Senior Citizen
Approx Nº of Visitors P.A.: 10,000
Gauge: Standard
Web: www.lincolnshirewoldsrailway.co.uk

GENERAL INFORMATION

Nearest Mainline Station: Grimsby (8 miles)
Nearest Bus Stop: Ludborough (½ mile)
Car Parking: Available at Ludborough Station only
Coach Parking: Space for 1 coach only
Souvenir Shop/Museum: Yes
Food & Drinks: Yes

SPECIAL INFORMATION

The LWR operates on a stretch of line which was once part of the Great Northern route from Boston to Grimsby. Heritage steam trains currently run between Ludborough and North Thoresby and work is now in progress to extend the line southwards towards Louth.

E-mail: contact@lincolnshirewoldsrailway.co.uk

OPERATING INFORMATION

Opening Times: 2017 dates: 26th March; 2nd, 15th, 16th, 17th & 30th April; 1st, 14th, 28th & 29th May; 11th, 18th & 25th June; 2nd, 9th, 16th, 23rd & 30th July; 2nd, 6th, 9th, 13th, 16th, 20th, 23rd, 27th & 28th August; 2nd, 3rd & 24th September (also 9th & 10th September for static viewing only); 8th, 22nd & 29th October; 5th & 19th November; Santa Specials (advance booking essential): 9th, 10th, 16th & 17th December. Also 1st January 2018.
Steam Working: All operating days except 24th September (Diesel Day event).
Prices: Adults £7.00   Children £4.00
Senior Citizens £5.00
Family £18.00 (2 adults + 4 children)
Different fares may apply at Special Events.
Otherwise, ticket prices shown offer unlimited rides.

Detailed Directions by Car:
The Railway is situated near Ludborough, ½ mile off the A16(T) Louth to Grimsby road. Follow the brown tourist signs for ½ mile to Fulstow to reach the station. Do not turn into Ludborough but stay on the bypass.

LLANGOLLEN RAILWAY

Address: The Station, Abbey Road, Llangollen, Denbighshire   LL20 8SN
Telephone N°: (01978) 860979
Year Formed: 1975
Location of Line: Valley of the River Dee from Llangollen to Corwen
Length of Line: 10 miles

N° of Steam Locos: 14   **Other Locos**: 13
N° of Members: 1,400
Annual Membership Fee: Adult £28.00; Family £39.00; Junior (under-16) £15.00
Approx N° of Visitors P.A.: 110,000
Gauge: Standard
Web Site: www.llangollen-railway.co.uk

Photograph courtesy of D.J. Smith

GENERAL INFORMATION

Nearest Mainline Station: Ruabon (6 miles)
Nearest Bus Station: Wrexham (12 miles)
Car Parking: Llangollen Royal International Pavilion (SatNav post code: LL20 8SW)
Coach Parking: Market Street car park in town centre (SatNav post code: LL20 8PS)
Souvenir Shop(s): Yes – at Llangollen Station
Food & Drinks: Yes – at Llangollen and Carrog and also at Berwyn and Glyndyfrdwy on Gala Days

SPECIAL INFORMATION

The route originally formed part of the line from Ruabon to Barmouth Junction which closed in 1964.

The railway has been rebuilt by volunteers since 1975 and now runs 10 miles through to Corwen.

OPERATING INFORMATION

Opening Times: 2017 dates: Services run daily from 18th February until 29th October. Please check the railway's web site for other out of season opening hours including Santa Specials which operate on weekends and other dates in December.
Steam Working: Please check the web site or contact the railway for details.
Prices: Adult Return £15.00   Child Return £8.00
Senior Citizen Return £13.50
Family Return £42.00 (2 adult + 2 child)
Note: Day Rover tickets are also available

Detailed Directions by Car:
From South & West: Go via the A5 to Llangollen. At the traffic lights turn into Castle Street to the River bridge; From North & East: Take the A483 to A539 junction and then via Trefor to Llangollen River bridge. The Station is adjacent to the River Dee.   SATNAV use LL20 8SN (but no parking available at the station).

LOCOMOTION – THE NATIONAL RAILWAY MUSEUM AT SHILDON

Address: Locomotion, Dale Road
Industrial Estate, Shildon   DL4 2RE
Telephone Nº: (01388) 777999
Fax Nº: (01388) 771448
Year Formed: 2004
Location: Shildon, County Durham

Length of Line: Over ½ mile
Nº of Steam Locos: 70+ locomotives and
other rail vehicles
Approx Nº of Visitors P.A.: 200,000
Gauge: Standard
Web site: www.nrm.org.uk/locomotion

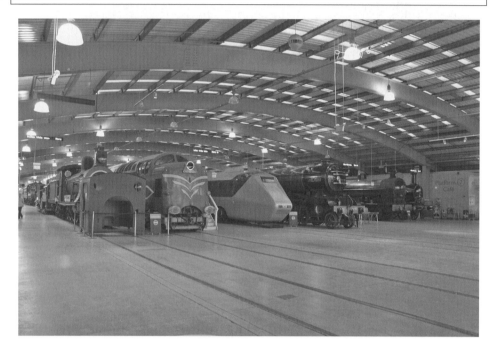

GENERAL INFORMATION

Nearest Mainline Station: Shildon (adjacent)
Nearest Bus Station: Durham
Car Parking: Available on site
Coach Parking: Available on site
Souvenir Shop(s): Yes
Food & Drinks: Yes

SPECIAL INFORMATION

This extensive site is the first regional branch of the
National Railway Museum and houses vehicles from
the National Collection in a purpose-built 6,000
square-foot building.

OPERATING INFORMATION

Opening Times: 2017 dates: Open daily but closed
from 24th to 26th December and on 1st January.
During the winter months (November to March),
the Museum is open from 10.00am to 4.00pm. The
whole site is open daily during the summer (1st
April to 31st October) – 10.00am to 5.00pm.
Steam Working: On special event days – contact
the museum or check the web site for further details.
Prices: Admission to the Museum is free of charge.
Train Rides: Adults £3.00
                        Concessions £2.00

Detailed Directions by Car:
From All Parts: Exit the A1(M) at Junction 58 and take the A68 and the A6072 to Shildon. Follow the Brown
tourist signs to Locomotion which is situated ¼ mile to the south-east of the Town Centre.
Drivers using SATNAVs should enter the following post code: DL4 2RE

MANGAPPS RAILWAY MUSEUM

Address: Southminster Road, Burnham-on-Crouch, Essex CM0 8QG	**N° of Steam Locos**: 6 (1 in service)
Telephone N°: (01621) 784898	**N° of Other Locos**: 12
Year Formed: 1989	**Approx N° of Visitors P.A.**: 22,000
Location of Line: Mangapps Farm	**Gauge**: Standard
Length of Line: ¾ mile	**Web site**: www.mangapps.co.uk
	E-mail: mangapps@tiscali.co.uk

GENERAL INFORMATION

Nearest Mainline Station: Burnham-on-Crouch (1 mile)
Nearest Bus Station: –
Car Parking: Ample free parking at site
Coach Parking: Ample free parking at site
Souvenir Shop(s): Yes
Food & Drinks: Yes – drinks and snacks only

SPECIAL INFORMATION

The Railway endeavours to recreate the atmosphere of an East Anglian light railway. It also includes an extensive museum with an emphasis on East Anglian items and signalling.

OPERATING INFORMATION

Opening Times: Closed during January then open every weekend and Bank Holiday from February to October inclusive. Also open daily during August. Santa Specials run during weekends in December. Please contact the railway for details of opening times during the School Holidays and for any other information.
Steam Working: Please contact the railway for details of steaming.
Prices: Adult – Steam £9.00; Diesel £8.00
Child – Steam £4.00; Diesel £3.50
Senior Citizen – Steam £8.00; Diesel £7.00
Note: Prices for special events may differ.

Detailed Directions by Car:
From South & West: From M25 take either the A12 or A127 and then the A130 to Rettendon Turnpike and then follow signs to Burnham; From North: From A12 take A414 to Oak Corner then follow signs to Burnham.

THE MIDDLETON RAILWAY

Address: The Station, Moor Road, Hunslet, Leeds LS10 2JQ	**N° of Steam Locos**: 17
Telephone N°: 0845 680-1758	**N° of Other Locos**: 13
Year Formed: 1960	**Annual Membership Fee**: Adults £20.00
Location of Line: Moor Road to Middleton Park	**Approx N° of Visitors P.A.**: 20,000
Length of Line: 1½ miles	**Gauge**: Standard
	Web Site: www.middletonrailway.org.uk

GENERAL INFORMATION

Nearest Mainline Station:
Leeds City (1 mile)
Nearest Bus Station: Leeds (1½ miles)
Car Parking: Free parking at site
Coach Parking: Free parking at site
Souvenir Shop(s): Yes
Food & Drinks: Yes

SPECIAL INFORMATION

The Middleton Railway is the oldest working railway in the world and was established in 1758 by Act of Parliament. The railway is also the first Standard Gauge line to be operated by volunteers and the first revenue-earning steam locomotive ran here in 1812. The railway also hosts a working museum housing a collection of Leeds built locomotives.

OPERATING INFORMATION

Opening Times: 2017 dates: Weekends and Bank Holidays from 25th March to the 19th November plus Santa Specials on weekends in December. Also open on Wednesdays in August. Services run approximately every 40 minutes from 11.00am to 4.00pm.
Steam Working: Diesels usually operate on Saturdays and on Wednesdays in August. All other services are usually steam-hauled including Santa Specials in December.
Prices: Adult £6.00   Child £2.50
                   Family £15.00
                       (2 adults + 3 children)
Tickets provide for unlimited travel on the day of issue. For a full timetable and details of special events, please check the railway's web site or phone 0845 680-1758.
Note: Different prices may apply on Special Event days.

Detailed Directions by Car:
From the South: Take the M621 Northbound and exit at Junction 5. Turn right at the top of the slip road and take the 3rd exit at the roundabout. The Railway is 50 yards on the right; From the West: Take the M621 Southbound and exit at Junction 6. Turn left at the end of the slip road then left again into Moor Road at the next set of traffic lights. Bear right at the mini roundabout and the railway is on the left after 150 yards.

MID-HANTS RAILWAY (WATERCRESS LINE)

Address: The Railway Station, Alresford, Hampshire SO24 9JG	**Nº of Steam Locos**: 17 (includes 'Thomas')
Telephone Nº: (01962) 733810	**Nº of Other Locos**: 5
Year Formed: 1977	**Nº of Members**: 5,100
Location of Line: Alresford to Alton	**Annual Membership Fee**: Adult £28.00
Length of Line: 10 miles	**Approx Nº of Visitors P.A.**: 120,000
	Gauge: Standard
	Web Site: www.watercressline.co.uk

Photo courtesy of David Warwick

GENERAL INFORMATION

Nearest Mainline Station: Alton (adjacent) or Winchester (7 miles)
Nearest Bus Station: Winchester or Alton
Car Parking: Pay and display at Alton and Alresford Stations (Alresford free on Sundays & Bank Holidays)
Coach Parking: By arrangement at Alresford Station
Souvenir Shop(s): At Alresford, Ropley & Alton
Food & Drinks: Yes – Buffet on most trains. 'West Country' buffet at Alresford

SPECIAL INFORMATION

The railway runs through four fully restored stations and has a Loco Yard and picnic area at Ropley.

OPERATING INFORMATION

Opening Times: 2017 dates: Weekends and Bank Holidays from March to 29th October plus Tuesday to Thursday from May to September.
Daily during the School holidays. Santa Specials run from Friday to Sunday during December and also on some other dates.
Steam Working: All operating days although a Steam/DMU combination is sometimes in service.
Prices: Adult £16.00
Child (ages 2 to 16) £8.00 (Under-2s free)
Family £40.00 (2 adults + 2 children)
Prices shown allow unlimited travel on the day of purchase. Prices may differ on Special Event days. A discount is available for pre-booked parties of 15 or more people. Write or call for a booking form.

Detailed Directions by Car:
From the East: Take the M25 then A3 and A31 to Alton; From the West: Exit the M3 at Junction 9 and take the A31 to Alresford Station.

MID-NORFOLK RAILWAY

Address: The Railway Station, Station Road, Dereham NR19 1DF
Telephone Nº: (01362) 690633
Talking Timetable Nº: (01362) 851723
Year Formed: 1995
Location: East Dereham to Wymondham
Length of Line: 11 miles

Nº of Steam Locos: Visiting locos only
Nº of Other Locos: 9
Nº of Members: 1,000
Annual Membership Fee: £19.00 (Adult)
Approx Nº of Visitors P.A.: 16,000
Gauge: Standard
Web site: www.mnr.org.uk

GENERAL INFORMATION

Nearest Mainline Station: Wymondham (1 mile)
Nearest Bus Station: Wymondham or East Dereham – each ½ mile away
Car Parking: Available at Dereham Station
Coach Parking: Available at Dereham Station
Souvenir Shop(s): Yes – at Dereham Station
Food & Drinks: Yes – at Dereham Station

SPECIAL INFORMATION

The Mid-Norfolk Railway aims to preserve the former Great Eastern Railway from Wymondham to County School. The section from Wymondham to Dereham was opened to passenger and freight traffic in May 1999 and clearance work is now complete on the East Dereham to County School section.

OPERATING INFORMATION

Opening Times: 2017 dates: Weekends and Bank Holidays from 1st April to 29th October. Also on Sundays in March, most Wednesdays from April to September and Thursdays from 29th June to 28th September. Also on some other dates during school holidays. Santa Specials run on dates in December.
Steam Working: Weekends from 7th May to 17th September and most Wednesdays in July and August. Please check with the railway before visiting.
Prices: Adult Return £10.00 (£14.00 in Summer)
Child Return £2.00 (£3.00 in Summer)
Senior Citizen Return £9.00
(£11.00 in Summer)
Family Ticket £20.00 (£28.00 in Summer)
Note: First Class tickets are also available

Detailed Directions by Car:
From All Parts: From the A47 bypass, turn into Dereham and follow the signs for the Town Centre. Turn right at the BP Garage – look out for the brown tourist signs – you will see the Station on your right.

MID-SUFFOLK LIGHT RAILWAY MUSEUM

Address: Brockford Station, Wetheringsett, Suffolk IP14 5PW	**Nº of Steam Locos**: 3 **Other Locos**: 1
Telephone Nº: (01449) 766899	**Nº of Members**: 400
Year Formed: 1990	**Annual Membership Fee**: £12.00
Location of Line: Wetheringsett, Suffolk	**Approx Nº of Visitors P.A.**: 2,000
Length of Line: ¼ mile	**Gauge**: Standard
	Web site: www.mslr.org.uk

GENERAL INFORMATION

Nearest Mainline Station: Stowmarket
Nearest Bus Station: Ipswich
Car Parking: Available on site
Coach Parking: Available by prior arrangement
Souvenir Shop(s): Yes
Food & Drinks: Yes

SPECIAL INFORMATION

The Mid-Suffolk Light Railway served the heart of the county for 50 years, despite being bankrupt before the first train ran. In a beautiful rural setting, the Museum seeks to preserve the memory of a unique branch line. The railway has now received planning permission for an extension which will more than double the length of the line and plans to open a new destination station, Aspall Halt.

OPERATING INFORMATION

Opening Times: 2017 dates: The museum is open on Sundays and Bank Holiday Mondays from 28th May to 28th August plus a Steam Gala on 9th and 10th September. Santa Specials run on 3rd, 9th, 10th, 16th, 17th December and on New Year's Day. Open from 11.00am to 5.00pm. Special events may open at different times. Please contact the railway for details.
Steam Working: All operational days. Please contact the railway or check the web site for further information.
Prices: Adult £10.00   Child £4.00 (Under-5s free)
    Family Ticket £24.00   Concession £8.00
Tickets allow unlimited travel on the day of issue and act as season tickets for the calendar year (subject to conditions). Special Event days have higher prices.

Detailed Directions by Car:
The Museum is situated 14 miles north of Ipswich and 28 miles south of Norwich, just off the A140. Look for Mendlesham TV mast and then follow the brown tourist signs from the A140.

MIDLAND RAILWAY – BUTTERLEY

Address: Butterley Station, Ripley, Derbyshire DE5 3QZ **Telephone Nº**: (01773) 747674 **Year Formed**: 1969 **Location of Line**: Butterley, near Ripley **Length of Line**: Standard gauge 3½ miles, Narrow gauge 0.8 mile	**Nº of Steam Locos**: 15 (+25 Other Locos) **Nº of Members**: 2,000 **Annual Membership Fee**: £20.00 (Adult) **Approx Nº of Visitors P.A.**: 130,000 **Gauge**: Standard, various Narrow gauges and miniature **Web**: www.midlandrailway-butterley.co.uk

GENERAL INFORMATION

Nearest Mainline Station: Alfreton (6 miles)
Nearest Bus Station: Bus stop outside Butterley Station.
Car Parking: Free parking at site – ample space
Coach Parking: Free parking at site
Souvenir Shop(s): Yes – at Butterley and Swanwick
Food & Drinks: Yes – both sites + bar on train

SPECIAL INFORMATION

The Centre is a unique project with a huge Museum development together with narrow gauge, miniature & model railways as well as a country park. Includes an Award-winning Victorian Railwayman's church and Princess Royal Class Locomotive Trust Depot.

OPERATING INFORMATION

Opening Times: 2017 dates: Trains run daily during Easter, all School Holidays and daily from 27th July to 3rd September. Also on most weekends throughout the year and for Santa Specials on dates in November and December. Please check the web site for further information.
Steam Working: Weekends and bank holidays throughout the year and most days in the school holidays. Please phone (01773) 570140 for details.
Prices: Adults £11.50 – £15.50
  Children £5.75 – £7.75
  Family £28.75 – £38.75
    (2 adults + 3 children)
Prices vary depending on the event being run.

Detailed Directions by Car:
From All Parts: From the M1 exit at Junction 28 and take the A38 towards Derby. The Centre is signposted at the junction with the B6179.

NATIONAL RAILWAY MUSEUM – YORK

Address: National Railway Museum,
Leeman Road, York   YO26 4XJ
Telephone Nº: 08448 153139
Year Formed: 1975
Location of Line: York
Length of Line: Short demonstration line

Nº of Steam Locos: 79
Nº of Other Locos: 37
Approx Nº of Visitors P.A.: 900,000
Web site: www.nrm.org.uk

GENERAL INFORMATION

Nearest Mainline Station: York (¼ mile)
Nearest Bus Station: York (¼ mile)
Car Parking: On site long stay car park
Coach Parking: On site
Souvenir Shop(s): Yes
Food & Drinks: Excellent on-site catering facilities.

SPECIAL INFORMATION

The Museum is the greatest of its kind in the world, housing the Nation's collection of locomotives, carriages, uniforms, posters and an extensive photographic archive. Special events and exhibitions run throughout the year. A 7¼ inch miniature railway offers rides in the South Yard area.

OPERATING INFORMATION

Opening Times: Open daily 10.00am to 6.00pm (or 5.00pm during the winter months). Closed from 24th to 26th of December.
Steam Working: School holidays – please phone to confirm details
Prices: Free admission but visitors are invited to make a donation. (Excludes some Special events and Steam rides). Phone 08448 153139 for details.

Detailed Directions by Car:
The Museum is located in the centre of York, just behind the Railway Station. It is clearly signposted from all approaches to York.

NENE VALLEY RAILWAY

Address: Wansford Station, Stibbington, Peterborough PE8 6LR	**Nº of Steam Locos**: 16
Telephone Nº: (01780) 784444	**Nº of Other Locos**: 14
E-mail: nvrorg@nvr.org.uk	**Nº of Members**: 1,300
Year Formed: 1977	**Annual Membership Fee**: Adult £25.00; Child/Senior £15.00; Family £40.00
Location: Off A1 to west of Peterborough	**Approx Nº of Visitors P.A.**: 65,000
Length of Line: 7½ miles	**Gauge**: Standard
	Web site: www.nvr.org.uk

GENERAL INFORMATION

Nearest Mainline Station: Peterborough (¾ mile)
Nearest Bus Station: Peterborough (Queensgate – ¾ mile)
Car Parking: Free parking at Wansford & Orton Mere
Coach Parking: Free coach parking at Wansford
Souvenir Shop(s): Yes
Food & Drinks: Yes

SPECIAL INFORMATION

The railway is truly international in flavour with British and Continental locomotives and rolling stock.

OPERATING INFORMATION

Opening Times: 2017 dates: Most weekends and Bank Holidays from March to December. Also open on most Wednesdays from May to September, most other days in the School summer holidays and at various other times. Santa Specials run in November & December. Please contact the Railway for further details. Trains run from 10.00am to as late as 5.00pm, depending on the time of the year.
Steam Working: Most services are steam hauled apart from on diesel days and times of high fire risk.
Prices: Adult £16.00   Child £8.00
        Family £40.00 (2 adults + 3 children)
        Senior Citizens/Disabled £13.00

Detailed Directions by Car:
The railway is situated off the southbound carriageway of the A1 between the A47 and A605 junctions – west of Peterborough and south of Stamford.

NORTH NORFOLK RAILWAY (THE POPPY LINE)

Address: Sheringham Station, Sheringham, Norfolk NR26 8RA
Telephone Nº: (01263) 820800
E-mail: enquiries@nnrailway.co.uk
Year Formed: 1975
Location of Line: Sheringham to Holt via Weybourne

Length of Line: 5½ miles
Nº of Steam Locos: 5 (+ visiting locos)
Nº of Other Locos: 4
Approx Nº of Visitors P.A.: 166,000
Gauge: Standard
Web site: www.nnrailway.co.uk

GENERAL INFORMATION

Nearest Mainline Station: Sheringham (200 yards)
Nearest Bus Station: Outside the Station
Car and Coach Parking:
Adjacent to Sheringham and Holt
Souvenir Shop(s): Available at all stations
Food & Drinks: Yes – main catering facilities at Sheringham Station. Light refreshments elsewhere.

SPECIAL INFORMATION

Lunch and evening dinner trains are scheduled throughout the year. Please check the website for times and fares. Weybourne Station is licensed for weddings.

OPERATING INFORMATION

Opening Times: 2017 dates: Daily from 1st April to 29th October. Also during weekends in March and November with Santa specials during December. 2017 Special events: Steam Gala 21st to 23rd April; Thomas 29th April to 1st May; Dads Army Live 28th & 29th May; Diesel Gala 9th to 12th June;

Tracks and Trenches 24th & 25th June; Vintage Transport Festival 1st & 2nd July with Suburban week operating alongside from 1st to 9th July then Beer Festival 14th to 16th July. Grand Steam Gala 1st to 3rd September then the 1940's Weekend 16th & 17th September. Halloween Week 21st to 29th October; Santa Specials on 2nd, 3rd, 9th, 10th, 16th 17th and 20th to 24th December; Mince Pie specials operate from 26th December to 1st January 2018.
Steam Working: 9.55am to 5.00pm (during high season)
Prices: Adult £12.50
  Child £9.00   (Under-5s travel free)
  Family £42.00 (2 adults + 2 children)
  Senior Citizens £11.50
  Dogs and Bicycles £2.00 each
The prices shown above are for all-day hop-on, hop-off, Day Rover tickets.
Special Events may have different prices.

Detailed Directions by Car:
Sheringham Station is situated just off the A149. Holt Station is located at High Kelling, just off the A148.

NORTH TYNESIDE STEAM RAILWAY

Address: Stephenson Railway Museum, Middle Engine Lane, North Shields, NE29 8DX **Telephone N°:** (0191) 200-7146 **Year Formed:** 1986 **Location:** Stephenson Railway Museum **Length of Line:** 1½ miles	**N° of Steam Locos:** 5 **N° of Other Locos:** 3 **N° of Members:** 30 **Annual Membership Fee:** £9.00 **Approx N° of Visitors P.A.:** 30,000 **Gauge:** Standard **Web site:** www.ntsra.org.uk

GENERAL INFORMATION

Nearest Mainline Station: Newcastle Central (5 miles) or for the Metro Percy Main (1½ miles)
Nearest Bus Station: North Shields
Car Parking: Free parking available on site
Coach Parking: Free parking available on site
Souvenir Shop(s): Yes
Food & Drinks: Hot drinks machine available

SPECIAL INFORMATION

A programme of events and activities is available from the Museum on request. Use the following URL:

www.twmuseums.org.uk/stephenson

OPERATING INFORMATION

Opening Times: 2017 dates: Sundays and Bank Holidays from Easter to 28th October and daily during School Holidays, 11.30am to 3.00pm. Santa Specials operate on most weekends in December and also from 20th to 22nd December.
Steam Working: Sundays and Bank Holiday Mondays from June to September.
Prices: Adult Day Rover   £6.00
  Child/Concessionary Day Rover £4.00
  Family Day Rover £15.00
  (2 Adults + 2 Children)
Note: Admission to the museum is free of charge and Season Tickets are also available.

Detailed Directions by Car:
The Railway is adjacent to the Silverlink Retail Park approximately ½ mile from the junction between the A19 and A1058. From the A19/A1058 junction look for the signs for 'Silverlink' before following the Brown tourist signs to the Stephenson Railway Museum.

NORTH YORKSHIRE MOORS RAILWAY

Address: Pickering Station, Pickering, North Yorkshire YO18 7AJ	**Nº of Other Locos**: 14
Telephone Nº: (01751) 472508 (enquiries)	**Nº of Members**: 10,330
Year Formed: 1967	**Annual Membership Fee**: Adult £31.00; Senior £29.00; Junior £15.00
Location of Line: Pickering to Grosmont via stations at Levisham and Goathland	**Approx Nº of Visitors P.A.**: 350,000
Length of Line: 18 miles	**Gauge**: Standard
Nº of Steam Locos: 20	**Web site**: www.nymr.co.uk
	E-mail: info@nymr.co.uk

GENERAL INFORMATION

Nearest Mainline Station: Grosmont (adjacent to the NYMR station) or Whitby
Nearest Bus Station: Pickering (½ mile)
Car Parking: Available at each station
Coach Parking: Available at Pickering & Grosmont
Souvenir Shop(s): Yes – at Pickering, Goathland, and Grosmont Stations plus Grosmont MPD
Food & Drinks: Pickering, Grosmont & Goathland. Also at Levisham on weekends and bank holidays.

SPECIAL INFORMATION

The NYMR runs through the spectacular North York Moors National Park and is the most popular heritage railway in the country. As seen in 'Heartbeat' and the first Harry Potter film. The railway operates extended services to and from Whitby.

OPERATING INFORMATION

Opening Times: 2017 dates: Open daily from 3rd April to 31st October. Santa Specials operate on 2nd, 3rd, 9th, 10th, 16th, 17th, 19th & 20th December. A Winter Timetable then operates from 26th December to 1st January 2018 and 10th to 18th February 2018.
Steam Working: Please contact the railway for scheduled locomotive listings.
Prices: Adult Day Rover £24.00 – £31.00
Child Day Rover £12.00 – £15.50
Senior Citizen Day Rover £20.40 – £26.35
Family Day Rover Tickets £50.00 – £65.00
(2 adults and 2 or 3 children options)

Detailed Directions by Car:
From the South: Follow the A64 past York to the Malton bypass then take the A169 to Pickering; From the North: Take A171 towards Whitby then follow the minor road through Egton to Grosmont.

NORTHAMPTON & LAMPORT RAILWAY

Address: Pitsford & Bramford Station, Pitsford Road, Chapel Brampton, Northampton NN6 8BA
Telephone Nº: (01604) 820327 (infoline)
Year Formed: 1983 (became operational in November 1995)
Length of Line: 1½ miles at present

Nº of Steam Locos: 5   **Nº Other Locos:** 4
Nº of Members: 350
Annual Membership Fee: Adult £15.00 and Senior Citizen £6.00
Approx Nº of Visitors P.A.: 9,300
Gauge: Standard
Web site: www.nlr.org.uk

GENERAL INFORMATION

Nearest Mainline Station: Northampton (5 miles)
Nearest Bus Station: Northampton (5 miles)
Car Parking: Free parking at site
Coach Parking: Free parking at site
Souvenir Shop(s): Yes
Food & Drinks: Yes

SPECIAL INFORMATION

The railway operates on a section of the old London & North Western Railway line between Northampton and Market Harborough and became operational again on 18th November 1995. Work is currently underway on a southern extension to the line.

OPERATING INFORMATION

Opening Times: 2017 dates: Sundays and Bank holidays from 26th March until 17th October and Santa Specials on most weekends in December. Open from 10.30am to 4.30pm (the last train runs at 3.30pm). Please contact the railway for a more detailed timetable.
Steam Working: Bank Holiday weekends and Santa Specials in December. Steam and Diesel trains run on alternating Sundays during other times. Please contact the railway for further information.
Prices: Adult £5.20
Child £4.20 (Under-2s ride free)
Family £16.50 (2 adults + 2 children)
Senior Citizen £4.20
Fares may vary on Special Event days.

Detailed Directions by Car:
The station is situated along the Pitsford road at Chapel Brampton, approximately 5 miles north of Northampton. Heading north out of town, it is signposted to the right on the A5199 (A50) Welford Road at Chapel Brampton crossroads or on the left on the A508 Market Harborough road at the Pitsford turn.

PEAK RAIL PLC

Address: Matlock Station, Matlock, Derbyshire DE4 3NA	**Nº of Steam Locos:** 8 **Other Locos:** 40+
Telephone Nº: (01629) 580381	**Nº of Members:** 1,700
Fax Nº: (01629) 760645	**Annual Adult Membership Fee:** £16.00
Year Formed: 1975	**Approx Nº of Visitors P.A.:** 150,000
Location: Matlock to Rowsley South	**Gauge:** Standard
Length of Line: Approximately 4½ miles	**Web site:** www.peakrail.co.uk
	E-mail: peakrail@peakrail.co.uk

GENERAL INFORMATION

Nearest Mainline Station: Matlock
Nearest Bus Station: Matlock
Car Parking: Paid car parking at Matlock Station. 200 free parking spaces available at Rowsley South Station and 20 free spaces at Darley Dale Station
Coach Parking: Free parking at Rowsley South
Souvenir Shop(s): Yes
Food & Drinks: Yes – R.M.B. Buffet on the train and the Rowsley Buffet at Rowsley South Station.

SPECIAL INFORMATION

The Palatine Restaurant Car is available whilst travelling on the train and caters for Sunday Lunches, Teas and Party Bookings. Coach parties are welcomed when the railway is operating.

OPERATING INFORMATION

Opening Times: Weekends and Bank Holidays throughout the year but closed during January and February. Also Tuesdays and Wednesdays from April to the end of September and Thursdays in August. Santa Specials run during weekends in December. Please contact the railway for further information. First departure from Rowsley South Station is 11.00am, last train departs at 3.56pm.
Steam Working: All services throughout the year.
Prices: Adult Return £8.50
Children – Ages 3-5 £2.50 (Under-3s free)
Children – Ages 6-15 £4.50
Senior Citizen Return £7.00
Family Ticket £26.50
(2 adults + 3 children)

Detailed Directions by Car:
Exit the M1 at Junctions 28, 29 or 30 and follow signs towards Matlock. From North and South take A6 direct to Matlock. From Stoke-on-Trent, take the A52 to Ashbourne, then the A5035 to Matlock. Upon reaching Matlock follow the brown tourist signs.

PLYM VALLEY RAILWAY

Address: Marsh Mills Station, Coypool Road, Plympton, Plymouth PL7 4NW	**No of Steam Locos**: 3
Telephone No: 07580 689380	**No of Other Locos**: 4
Year Formed: 1980	**No of Members**: 250
Location of Line: Marsh Mills to Plym Bridge Platform	**Annual Membership Fee**: £12.00
	Approx No of Visitors P.A.: 5,000
Length of Line: 1¼ mile	**Gauge**: Standard
	Web site: www.plymrail.co.uk

GENERAL INFORMATION

Nearest Mainline Station: Plymouth (4 miles)
Nearest Bus Station: Plymouth (3 miles)
Car Parking: Available on site
Coach Parking: Available on site
Souvenir Shop(s): Yes
Food & Drinks: Light snacks available

SPECIAL INFORMATION

2012 saw the opening of the extension of the line to Plym Bridge. This is a section of the former Great Western branch line which from Tavistock Junction through to Launceston. The railway now plans to further develop their visitor facilities at Marsh Mills.

OPERATING INFORMATION

Opening Times: Open for static viewing on most Sundays from 11.00am to 5.00pm and brake van rides are also available on most Sundays except when trains are running. 2017 train dates: 16th & 28th April; 14th May; 4th & 18th June; 2nd, 16th & 30th July; 13th & 27th August; 3rd & 17th September; 29th October plus Santa Specials on 3rd, 10th and 16th, 18th & 20th December. Also some Evening Dining Trains (booking required). Please check the web site for details and times.
Steam Working: Please contact the railway for details.
Prices: Adult Return £4.00   Day Rover £6.00
              Child Return £2.00   Day Rover £3.00
Note: There is no charge to visit the station.

Detailed Directions by Car:
Leave the A38 at the Marsh Mills turn-off and take the B3416 towards Plympton. Turn left into Coypool Road just after the McDonalds restaurant. From Plymouth City Centre, take the A374 to Marsh Mills, then as above.

PONTYPOOL & BLAENAVON RAILWAY

Address: 33 Broad Street, Blaenavon, Torfaen NP4 9ND
e-mail: info@pbrly.co.uk
Telephone Nº: (01495) 792263 (Shop)
Year Formed: 1980 (Opened 1983)
Location of Line: Just off the B4248 between Blaenavon and Brynmawr
Length of Line: 3½ miles

Nº of Steam Locos: 6
Nº of Other Locos: 5 + 4 DMUs
Nº of Members: 350
Annual Membership Fee: £15.00
Approx Nº of Visitors P.A.: 16,500
Gauge: Standard
Web site: www.pbrly.co.uk

GENERAL INFORMATION

Nearest Mainline Station: Abergavenny (5 miles)
Nearest Bus Station: Blaenavon Town (1½ miles) – regular bus service within ¼ mile (except Sundays)
Car Parking: Free parking for 50 cars on site
Coach Parking: Available on site
Souvenir Shop(s): Yes – at the Station and also a shop at 33 Broad Street, Blaenavon
Food & Drinks: Light refreshments on the train and at the station.

SPECIAL INFORMATION

The railway operates over very steep gradients, is run entirely by volunteers and is the highest standard gauge preserved railway in England and Wales.

OPERATING INFORMATION

Opening Times: 2017 dates: Every weekend and Bank Holiday Monday from 1st April to 24th September. Also 28th, 29th & 31st October, Wednesdays from 26th July to 23rd August and Santa Specials on weekends in December. Please check the web site for further details.
Steam Working: Trains are steam-hauled during Peak days and special steam days during May and June. Diesel locos may be used on quiet days. Please contact the Railway for further information.
Prices: Adult Day Rover £9.00 (Concessions £8.00)
        Child Day Rover £5.00
        Family Day Rover £23.00 (2 adult + 3 child)
Note: Fares may vary on Special Event days.

Detailed Directions by Car:
From All Parts: The railway is situated just off the B4248 between Blaenavon and Brynmawr and is well signposted as you approach Blaenavon. Use Junction 25A if using the M4 from the East, or Junction 26 from the West. Head for Pontypool. From the Midlands use the M50, A40 then A465 to Brynmawr. From North & West Wales consider using the 'Heads of the Valleys' A465 to Brynmawr. As you approach the Railway, look out for the Colliery water tower – you can't miss it!

RIBBLE STEAM RAILWAY

Address: Chain Caul Road, Preston, PR2 2PD	**Nº of Steam Locos:** 35
Telephone Nº: (01772) 728800	**Nº of Other Locos:** 22
Year Formed: 2005	**Nº of Members:** 400
Location: West of Preston City Centre	**Annual Membership Fee:** £15.00
Length of Line: 3 mile round trip	**Approx Nº of Visitors P.A.:** 20,000+
	Gauge: Standard
	Web site: www.ribblesteam.org.uk

GENERAL INFORMATION

Nearest Mainline Station: Preston (2 miles)
Nearest Bus Station: Preston (2 miles)
Car Parking: Available on site
Coach Parking: Available on site
Souvenir Shop(s): Yes
Food & Drinks: Available

SPECIAL INFORMATION

The line traverses a swing bridge across the Marina entrance – the only preserved steam line in Britain to have such a feature! The railway also has the largest collection of standard gauge industrial locomotives housed under cover in the UK.

OPERATING INFORMATION

Opening Times: 2017 dates: Open 10.30am to 5.00pm on dates in April then weekends and Bank Holidays from 6th May to 1st October. Also open for Santa specials on weekends in December. Please contact the railway for details of further operating days.
Steam Working: On all days when the railway is open to the public. Trains run hourly from 11.00am to 4.00pm.
Prices: Adult Return £7.00
          Child/Concessionary Return £4.50
          Family Return £20.00
Note: Special event prices may differ to those shown.

Detailed Directions by Car:
From All Parts: The Railway is located on the Riversway/Docklands Business and Residential Park, just off the A583 Lytham/Blackpool road and approximately 1½ miles to the west of Preston City Centre. Follow the Brown Tourist signs from the A583 for the railway.

ROCKS BY RAIL –
THE LIVING IRONSTONE MUSEUM

Address: Ashwell Road, Cottesmore, Oakham, Rutland LE15 7FF	**Nº of Steam Locos**: 12
Telephone Nº: 07974 171068	**Nº of Other Locos**: 12
	Nº of Members: 275
Year Formed: 1979	**Annual Membership Fee**: £10.00
Location of Line: Between the villages of Cottesmore and Ashwell	**Approx Nº of Visitors P.A.**: 8,000
	Gauge: Standard
Length of Line: ¾ mile	**Web site**: www.rocks-by-rail.org

GENERAL INFORMATION

Nearest Mainline Station: Oakham (4 miles)
Nearest Bus Station: Cottesmore/Ashwell (1½ miles)
Car Parking: Available at the site
Coach Parking: Limited space available
Souvenir Shop(s): None
Food & Drinks: Available on Thursdays and Sundays from Easter to October.

SPECIAL INFORMATION

This Industrial Railway Heritage centre is located at the end of the former Ashwell-Cottesmore mineral branch and is based at the former exchange sidings.

OPERATING INFORMATION

Opening Times: 2017 dates: Static viewing on Tuesdays and Thursdays from 10.00am to 4.00pm throughout the year and also on Sundays from Easter to November. The Rutlander Train operates on the third Sunday of the month from Easter to November and also on Bank Holidays. Also open with the 'Driver for a Fiver' offer (Diesel loco) on the second Sunday each month, Easter to November.
Steam Working: 3rd Sunday each month, Easter to November, with brake van rides 11.00am to 4.00pm.
Prices: Adults £8.00   Children £5.00 (ages 3-14)
           Concessions £7.00
           Family Ticket £25.00 (2 adults + 3 children)

Detailed Directions by Car:
From All Parts: The Museum is situated 4 miles north of Oakham between Ashwell and Cottesmore. Follow the brown tourist signs from the B668 Oakham to A1 road or the signs from the A606 Stamford to Oakham Road.

ROYAL DEESIDE RAILWAY

Address: Milton of Crathes, Crathes, Banchory AB31 5QH	**Nº of Steam Locos**: 2
Telephone Nº: (01330) 844416	**Nº of Other Locos**: 3
E-mail: info@deeside-railway.co.uk	**Nº of Members**: 250
Year Formed: 1996	**Annual Membership Fee**: £20.00
Location of Line: Milton of Crathes	**Approx Nº of Visitors P.A.**: 12,000
Length of Line: 1 mile	**Gauge**: Standard
	Web site: www.deeside-railway.co.uk

GENERAL INFORMATION

Nearest Mainline Station: Aberdeen (14 miles)
Nearest Bus Station: Stagecoach Bluebird bus stop nearby on A93.
Car Parking: Free parking available on site
Coach Parking: Free parking available on site
Souvenir Shop(s): Yes
Food & Drinks: Yes – inside the restored Victorian station and also inside a static catering car.

SPECIAL INFORMATION

The line is gradually being extended to Banchory and, when completed, will be 2 miles in length.

OPERATING INFORMATION

Opening Times: 2017 dates: Weekends and some Bank Holidays from Easter to September plus Wednesdays in July and early August and some other dates. Also open for Santa Specials each weekend in December and the last weekend in November. Please contact the railway for further information.
Steam Working: Please contact the railway for details of steaming dates.
Prices: Adults £4.00 (£6.00 Steam days)
  Children £2.00 (£3.00 Steam days)
  Senior Citizens £2.50 (£4.00 Steam days)
Note: Day Rover tickets are also available.

Detailed Directions by Car:
From the South: Take the A90 to Stonehaven. Exit onto the B979 for Stonehaven and follow into the town square. Turn left at the traffic lights and follow signs for the A957 to Banchory (Historic Slug Road). Follow this road for 14 mile via Durris to Crathes and the junction with the A93. Turn left and follow the Brown Tourist signs, turning left for the railway after approximately 600 yards; From the North & West: Follow the A980 to Banchory and turn left onto the A93. Turn right following the Brown Tourist signs for the railway.

RUSHDEN TRANSPORT MUSEUM

Address: Rushden Station, Station Approach, Rushden, NN10 0AW	**Nº of Steam Locos**: 3
Telephone Nº: (01933) 353111	**Nº of Other Locos**: 5
Year Formed: 1985	**Nº of Members**: Approximately 650
Location of Line: Rushden, Northants.	**Annual Membership Fee**: £20.00 (Family)
Length of Line: ½ mile (each paid trip is 2½ miles in distance)	**Approx Nº of Visitors P.A.**: 5,000
	Gauge: Standard
	Web site: www.rhts.co.uk

GENERAL INFORMATION

Nearest Mainline Station: Wellingborough (5 miles)
Nearest Bus Station: Northampton (14 miles)
Car Parking: Available on site. On operating days a nearby public car park must be used.
Coach Parking: None
Souvenir Shop(s): Yes
Food & Drinks: Available on operating weekends

SPECIAL INFORMATION

The Rushden Transport Museum is situated in the old Midland Railway Station of 1894 which once formed part of the Wellingborough to Higham Ferrers branch line. Taken over by the Rushden Historical Transport Society in 1984 the station also provides the society with a social club.

OPERATING INFORMATION

Opening Times: The Museum is open from Easter until the end of October on Saturdays (2.00pm to 4.00pm), Sundays (11.00am to 4.00pm) and most Fridays (2.00pm to 4.00pm). A variety of special events are scheduled for 2017. For further details, either check the museum's web site or phone for information.
Steam Working: Trains are operated by The Rushden, Higham & Wellingborough Railway at various events throughout the year. Please contact the museum for further details.
Prices: Admission to the museum is usually free but charges will be made on Special Event days.

Detailed Directions by Car:
From All Parts: Take the A6 to the Rushden Bypass (to the south of the A45) and turn into John Clark Way by the large grey warehouses. The Station is located on the right-hand side of the road after approximately 400 yards.

SCOTTISH INDUSTRIAL RAILWAY CENTRE

Address: Dunaskin, Dalmellington Road, Waterside, Patna, Ayrshire   KA6 7JF
Telephone Nº: (01292) 313579 (Evenings & Weekends)
Year Formed: 1974
Location of Line: Dunaskin Ironworks
Length of Line: A third of a mile
Web site: www.scottishindustrialrailwaycentre.org.uk

Nº of Steam Locos: 9
Nº of Other Locos: 15
Nº of Members: 180
Annual Membership Fee: £20.00
Approx Nº of Visitors P.A.: 3,500
Gauge: Standard

GENERAL INFORMATION

Nearest Mainline Station: Ayr (10 miles)
Nearest Bus Station: ½ hourly bus service from Ayr – phone (01292) 613500 for more information
Car Parking: Free parking available at the site
Coach Parking: Free parking available at the site
Souvenir Shop(s): Yes
Food & Drinks: Cafe now available on site

SPECIAL INFORMATION

The Railway is operated by the Ayrshire Railway Preservation Group and is located at the very last engine shed to be built in the UK to service steam locomotives, constructed in 1964.

OPERATING INFORMATION

Opening Times: 2017 operating dates: 30th April; 1st, 28th & 29th May; 25th June; 2nd, 9th, 16th, 17th, 23rd & 30th July; 6th, 13th, 20th & 27th August; 24th September. Open from 11.00am to 4.30pm on these days (last admission at 4.00pm). The site is closed at all other times. Please contact the railway or check the web site for further details.
Steam Working: On all operating dates.
Prices: Adults £6.00
Children £4.00 (Free for ages 3 and under)
Senior Citizens £4.00
Family Ticket £16.00 (2 adults + 3 children)

Detailed Directions by Car:
From All Parts: Dunaskin is situated adjacent to the A713 Ayr to Castle Douglas road, approximately 10 miles to the southwest of Ayr.

SEVERN VALLEY RAILWAY

Correspondence Address: Number One Comberton Place, Kidderminster DY10 1QR	**Nº of Steam Locos:** 27
	Nº of Other Locos: 12
	Nº of Members: 13,000
Telephone Nº: (01562) 757900	**Annual Membership Fee:** Adult £22.00
Year Formed: 1965	**Approx Nº of Passengers P.A.:** 250,000
Location of Line: Kidderminster (Worcs.) to Bridgnorth (Shropshire)	**Gauge:** Standard
	Web site: www.svr.co.uk
Length of Line: 16 miles	

GENERAL INFORMATION

Nearest Mainline Station: Kidderminster (adjacent)
Nearest Bus Station: Kidderminster (500 yards)
Car Parking: Large car park at Kidderminster. Spaces also available at other stations.
Coach Parking: At Kidderminster
Souvenir Shop(s): At Kidderminster & Bridgnorth
Food & Drinks: On most trains. Also at Bewdley, Bridgnorth, Kidderminster and The Engine House

SPECIAL INFORMATION

The SVR has numerous special events including an Autumn Steam Gala, 1940's weekend, Classic Car & Bike Day and visits by Santa! 'The Engine House', the railway's visitor and education centre, is a further attraction at Highley.

OPERATING INFORMATION

Opening Times: 2017 dates: Weekends from mid-February to November. Also daily from 1st April to 1st October and during local School Holidays. Santa Specials run at weekends and on some other dates in December. Please contact the railway for further details.
Steam Working: Train times vary depending on timetable information. Phone for details.
Prices: Adult Day Rover £19.80
                 Child Day Rover £13.00
                 Senior Citizen Day Rover £18.80
Note: Entrance to The Engine House is included in the above prices and upgrades to First Class travel are also available. Discounts are available for advance bookings.

Detailed Directions by Car:
For Kidderminster exit the M5 at Junction 3 or Junction 6 and follow the brown tourist signs for the railway; From the South: Take the M40 then M42 to Junction 1 for the A448 to Kidderminster.   SATNAV DY10 1QX

SOMERSET & DORSET RAILWAY TRUST MUSEUM

Address: The Railway Station, Washford, Somerset TA23 0PP
Telephone Nº: (01984) 640869
Year Formed: 1966
Location of Line: Washford Station
Length of Line: Station sidings only

Nº of Steam Locos: 2
Nº of Other Locos: 1
Annual Membership Fee: £18.00
Approx Nº of Visitors P.A.: 3,000
Gauge: Standard
Web site: www.sdrt.org.uk

GENERAL INFORMATION

Nearest Mainline Station: Taunton (17 miles)
Nearest Bus Station: Taunton (17 miles)
Car Parking: Available on site
Coach Parking: None
Souvenir Shop(s): Yes
Food & Drinks: None

SPECIAL INFORMATION

The Museum of the Somerset & Dorset Railway Trust contains a mass of exhibits about and memorabilia of this much loved line. This includes a reconstruction of Midford signal box and carriages and wagons including some undergoing restoration.

OPERATING INFORMATION

Opening Times: A full list of opening dates had not been set at the time of going to press. Please check the Museum's web site or phone for further details.
Steam Working: Please contact the Museum or check the web site for further details.
Prices: Admission to the Museum –
    Adult £2.00
    Child £1.00
    Family £5.00
Note: Additional charges may apply on Special Event days.

Detailed Directions by Car:
The Museum is located at the Railway Station in Washford Village on the A39 Bridgwater to Minehead road.

SOUTH DEVON RAILWAY

Address: Buckfastleigh Station, Buckfastleigh, Devon TQ11 0DZ	**Nº of Steam Locos:** 15
Telephone Nº: 01364 644370	**Nº of Other Locos:** 11
Year Formed: 1969	**Nº of Members:** 2,500
Location of Line: Totnes to Buckfastleigh via Staverton	**Annual Membership Fee:** £20.00
	Approx Nº of Visitors P.A.: 100,000+
Length of Line: 7 miles	**Gauge:** Standard
	Web Site: www.southdevonrailway.co.uk

GENERAL INFORMATION

Nearest Mainline Station: Totnes (¼ mile)
Nearest Bus Station: Totnes (½ mile), Buckfastleigh (Station Road)
Car Parking: Free parking at Buckfastleigh, Council/NR parking at Totnes
Coach Parking: As above
Souvenir Shop(s): Yes – at Buckfastleigh
Food & Drinks: Yes – at Buckfastleigh & on train

SPECIAL INFORMATION

The railway was opened in 1872 as the Totnes, Buckfastleigh & Ashburton Railway.

OPERATING INFORMATION

Opening Times: 2017 dates: Daily from 18th March to 29th October. Santa Specials also run on weekends and other dates during December. Please contact the railway for further details.
Steam Working: Almost all trains are steam hauled.
Prices: Adult Return £15.00   Child Return £9.00
Family Return £43.00
(2 adults + 2 children)
Senior Citizen Return £14.00
Note: Extra discounts are available for large groups.

E-mail: trains@southdevonrailway.org

Detailed Directions by Car:
Buckfastleigh is half way between Exeter and Plymouth on the A38 Devon Expressway. Totnes can be reached by taking the A385 from Paignton and Torquay. Brown tourist signs give directions for the railway.

SPA VALLEY RAILWAY

Address: West Station, Tunbridge Wells, Kent TN2 5QY **Telephone Nº:** (01892) 537715 **Year Formed:** 1985 **Location of Line:** Tunbridge Wells West to Groombridge and Eridge **Length:** 5 miles	**Nº of Steam Locos:** 9 **Nº of Other Locos:** 7 **Nº of Members:** Approximately 850 **Annual Membership Fee:** £20.00 **Approx Nº of Visitors P.A.:** 36,000 **Gauge:** Standard **Web Site:** www.spavalleyrailway.co.uk

GENERAL INFORMATION

Nearest Mainline Station: Eridge (cross-platform interchange with the mainline)
Nearest Bus Stop: Outside Sainsbury's (100yds)
Car Parking: Available in Tunbridge Wells nearby in Major Yorks Road, Union House & Linden Close
Coach Parking: Montacute Road (150 yards)
Souvenir Shop(s): Yes   **Food & Drinks:** Yes

SPECIAL INFORMATION

The Railway's Tunbridge Wells Terminus is in a historic and unique L.B. & S.C.R. engine shed. The extension to Eridge is now open at weekends and on public holidays and tickets inclusive of entry to Groombridge Place Gardens are also available.

OPERATING INFORMATION

Opening Times: 2017 dates: Weekends and Bank Holidays from February to October. Some weekdays during School Holidays, Thursdays from June to August and Tuesdays and Wednesdays from 25th July to 30th August. Also Santa Specials during on December weekends.
Steam Working: Services alternate between steam and diesel haulage. Trains run from 10.30am to 4.10pm with different times during midweek.
Prices: Adult Return £12.00   Child Return £6.00
       Senior Citizen Return £11.00
       Family Return £31.00 (2 adult + 2 child)
Fares vary on some special event days.
Fares allow unlimited travel on the day of issue except for special event days.

Detailed Directions by Car:
The Spa Valley Railway is in the southern part of Tunbridge Wells, 100 yards off the A26. Tunbridge Wells Station is adjacent to Sainsbury's and Homebase.   For Eridge Station (Satnav TN3 9LE), follow signs off the A26.

STEAM – MUSEUM OF THE GREAT WESTERN RAILWAY

Address: STEAM – Museum of the Great Western Railway, Firefly Avenue, Swindon   SN2 2EY
Telephone Nº: (01793) 466646
Year Formed: 2000

Nº of Steam Locos: 8
Nº of Other Locos: 1
Approx Nº of Visitors P.A.: 100,000
Web site: www.steam-museum.org.uk
E-mail: adminsteam@swindon.gov.uk

GENERAL INFORMATION

Nearest Mainline Station: Swindon (10 min. walk)
Nearest Bus Station: Swindon (10 minute walk)
Car Parking: Ample parking space available in the Outlet Centre (charges apply)
Coach Parking: Free parking on site and nearby
Souvenir Shop(s): Yes
Food & Drinks: There is a Café within the Museum

SPECIAL INFORMATION

STEAM tells the story of the men and women who built the Great Western Railway.

OPERATING INFORMATION

Opening Times: Open daily all year round from 11.00am to 5.00pm (4.00pm on Sundays. Last admission is 4.00pm (3.00pm on Sundays).
Closed from 24th to 26th December and 1st January.
Steam Working: During some special events only – please check the Museum web site for details.
Prices: Adult Tickets £8.90
Child Tickets £6.50
Family Tickets £15.50 – £33.00
Senior Citizen Tickets £7.15
Children under 3 are admitted free
Note: Season tickets are also available and prices for Special Events may be higher.

Detailed Directions by Car:
Exit the M4 at Junction 16 and follow the brown tourist signs to 'Outlet Centre'. Similarly follow the brown signs from all other major routes.   From the Railway Station: STEAM is a 10 to 15 minute walk and is accessible through the pedestrian tunnel – entrance by Emlyn Square.

THE STRATHSPEY RAILWAY

Address: Aviemore Station, Dalfaber Road, Aviemore PH22 1PY	**No of Steam Locos**: 7
Telephone No: (01479) 810725	**No of Other Locos**: 10
Year Formed: 1971	**No of Members**: 900
Location of Line: Aviemore to Boat of Garten and Broomhill, Inverness-shire	**Annual Membership Fee**: £24.00
	Approx No of Visitors P.A.: 60,000
Length of Line: 9½ miles at present	**Gauge**: Standard
	Web site: www.strathspeyrailway.co.uk

GENERAL INFORMATION

Nearest Mainline Station: Aviemore – Strathspey trains depart from Platform 3
Nearest Bus Station: Aviemore (adjacent)
Car Parking: Available at all stations
Coach Parking: Available at Aviemore and Broomhill stations
Souvenir Shop(s): Yes – at all stations
Food & Drinks: Available on most services

SPECIAL INFORMATION

Experience the stunning Scottish Highlands in a way like no other as the Railway wends its way through the stunning Cairngorm Mountains.

OPERATING INFORMATION

Opening Times: Daily in July and August. Weekends from mid-February to October. Wednesday and Thursday in April, May, June, September and October. Fridays in June and September and other dates in February and March. Winter Specials operate on dates in December and January. Please phone for details. Generally open from 10.30am to 4.30pm.
Steam Working: Most trains are steam-hauled but special diesel services are timetabled throughout the year. Please check the web site for further details.
Prices: Adult Return £14.25
          Child Return £7.15 (Under-5s free)
          Family Return £36.00
                (2 adults and up to 3 children)
          Senior Citizen Return £12.80
Note: Day Rover tickets are also available.

Detailed Directions by Car:
For Aviemore Station from South: Take the A9 then B970 and turn left between the railway & river bridges. For Boat of Garten from North; Take the A9 then A938 to Carr Bridge, then B9153 and A95 and follow the signs; From North East: Take A95 to Boat of Garten or Broomhill (3½ miles South from Grantown-on-Spey.

SWANAGE RAILWAY

Address: Station House, Railway Station, Swanage, Dorset BH19 1HB	**Nº of Steam Locos:** 5
Telephone Nº: (01929) 425800	**Nº of Other Locos:** 5
Year Formed: 1976	**Nº of Members:** 4,200
Location of Line: Swanage to Norden	**Annual Membership Fee:** Adult £21.00; Junior £12.00; Family £42.00
Length of Line: 6 miles	**Approx Nº of Visitors P.A.:** 216,000
Gauge: Standard	**Web site:** www.swanagerailway.co.uk

GENERAL INFORMATION

Nearest Mainline Station: Wareham (10 miles)
Nearest Bus Station: Swanage Station (adjacent)
Car Parking: Park & Ride at Norden. Public car parks in Swanage (5 minutes walk)
Coach Parking: Available at Norden
Souvenir Shop(s): Yes – at Swanage Station
Food & Drinks: Yes – buffet available on trains and also Swanage Station Buffet and at Norden.

SPECIAL INFORMATION

The railway runs along part of the route of the old Swanage to Wareham railway, opened in 1885.

OPERATING INFORMATION

Opening Times: 2017 dates: Weekends from 11th February then daily from 25th March to 29th October. Also open on a number of other dates throughout the year including Santa Specials in December. Usually open from 10.00am to around 5.00pm although trains may run later from May to September and evening services operate during some dates in the school summer holidays.
Steam Working: Most services are steam-hauled. Please check with the Railway for further details.
Prices: Adult Return £12.50
Child Return £7.60
Family Ticket £35.00
Note: Prices shown above are the maximum return fares and may be subject to change.

Detailed Directions by Car:
Norden Park & Ride Station is situated off the A351 on the approach to Corfe Castle. Swanage Station is situated in the centre of the town, just a few minutes walk from the beach. Take the A351 to reach Swanage.

SWINDON & CRICKLADE RAILWAY

Address: Blunsdon Station, Tadpole Lane, Blunsdon, Swindon, Wilts SN25 2DA	**N° of Steam Locos**: 6
Phone N°: (01793) 771615	**N° of Other Locos**: 9
Year Formed: 1978	**N° of Members**: 700
Location: Mouldon Hill to Hayes Knoll	**Annual Membership Fee**: £15.00
Length of Line: 2½ miles	**Approx N° of Visitors P.A.**: 16,000
	Gauge: Standard

GENERAL INFORMATION

Nearest Mainline Station: Swindon (5 miles)
Nearest Bus Station: Bus stop at Oakhurst (¾ mile)
Car Parking: Free parking at Blunsdon Station
Coach Parking: Free parking at Blunsdon Station
Souvenir Shop(s): Yes
Food & Drinks: Yes

SPECIAL INFORMATION

The Engine Shed at Hayes Knoll Station is
occasionally open to the public.

Web site: www.swindon-cricklade-railway.org

OPERATING INFORMATION

Opening Times: 2017 dates: The Railway is open
every weekend and Bank Holiday from Easter to late
November. Also on Wednesdays in August and
Sundays in November. Santa Specials run in
December and other various special events
throughout the year also have Steam train rides.
Open 10.30am to 4.00pm.
Steam Working: Every Sunday from Easter until the
end of October and certain other dates – please
contact the railway for further details.
Prices: Adult £8.00   Child £6.00
          Concessions £7.00   Family £24.00
Prices are different for Special Event days.

Detailed Directions by Car:
From the M4: Exit the M4 at Junction 15 and follow the A419. Turn left towards Blunsdon Stadium and follow
the signs for the Railway: From Cirencester: Follow the A419 to the top of Blunsdon Hill, then turn right and
follow signs for Blundson Stadium.

TANFIELD RAILWAY

Address: Marley Hill Engine Shed, Old Marley Hill, Gateshead, Tyne & Wear NE16 5ET	**Nº of Steam Locos:** 29 Standard, 2 Narrow
	Nº Other Locos: 12 Standard, 15 Narrow
	Nº of Members: 150
Telephone Nº: 0750 809-2365	**Annual Membership Fee:** £14.00 (Adult)
Year Formed: 1976	**Approx Nº of Visitors P.A.:** 40,000
Location of Line: Between Sunniside & East Tanfield, Co. Durham	**Gauge:** Standard and Narrow gauge
	Web site: www.tanfield-railway.co.uk
Length of Line: 3 miles	

GENERAL INFORMATION

Nearest Mainline Station: Newcastle-upon-Tyne (8 miles)
Nearest Bus St'n: Gateshead Interchange (6 miles)
Car Parking: Spaces for 150 cars at Andrews House and 100 spaces at East Tanfield
Coach Parking: Spaces for 6 or 7 coaches only
Souvenir Shop(s): Yes
Food & Drinks: Yes – light snacks only

SPECIAL INFORMATION

Tanfield Railway is the oldest existing railway in use – it was originally opened in 1725. It also runs beside The Causey Arch, the oldest railway bridge in the world.

OPERATING INFORMATION

Opening Times: Every Sunday & Bank Holiday Monday throughout the year. Also open on Thursdays and Saturdays during the Summer school holidays and for other events throughout the year. Santa Specials run on weekends and other dates in December and November.
Steam Working: Most trains are steam-hauled and run from 10.30am to 3.30pm (from 10.30am to 3.00pm during the Winter months).
Prices: Adult £10.00
         Child £6.00 (Under 5's travel free)
         Senior Citizen £7.00
         Family £26.00 (2 adults + 2 children)
Note: Special Event days may have higher prices.

Detailed Directions by Car:
Sunniside Station is off the A6076 Sunniside to Stanley road in Co. Durham. To reach the Railway, leave A1(M), follow signs for Beamish museum at Chester-le-Street then continue to Stanley and follow Tanfield Railway signs.

TELFORD STEAM RAILWAY

Address: The Old Loco Shed, Bridge Road, Horsehay, Telford, Shropshire
Telephone Enquiries: (01952) 503880
Year Formed: 1976
Location: Horsehay & Dawley Station
Length of Line: 1 mile standard gauge, an eighth of a mile 2 foot narrow gauge

Nº of Steam Locos: 5 (2 operational)
Nº of Other Locos: 12
Nº of Members: Approximately 220
Annual Membership Fee: £12.00
Approx Nº of Visitors P.A.: 10,000
Web site: www.telfordsteamrailway.co.uk

GENERAL INFORMATION

Nearest Mainline Station: Wellington or Telford Central
Nearest Bus Station: Dawley (1 mile)
Car Parking: Free parking at the site
Coach Parking: Free parking at the site
Souvenir Shop(s): 'Freight Stop Gift Shop'
Food & Drinks: 'The Furnaces' Tea Room

SPECIAL INFORMATION

Telford Steam Railway has both a Standard Gauge and Narrow Gauge line as well as Miniature and Model Railways. A major extension to the line has recently opened.

OPERATING INFORMATION

Opening Times: 2017 dates: Every Sunday and Bank Holiday between 15th April and 24th September. Santa Specials operate on dates during December. Open 11.00am to 4.30pm.
Steam Working: Most Bank Holidays. Please contact the railway for further information.
Prices: Adult all day tickets £6.00
Child all day tickets £4.00
Concession all day tickets £5.00
Family all day tickets £15.00
(2 adults + 2 children)
Note: Higher prices apply for special event days.

Detailed Directions by Car:
From All Parts: Exit the M54 at Junction 6, travel south along the A5223 then follow the brown tourist signs for the railway.

TYSELEY LOCOMOTIVE WORKS VISITOR CENTRE

Address: 670 Warwick Road, Tyseley, Birmingham   B11 2HL
Telephone Nº: (0121) 708-4960
Year Formed: 1969
Location of Museum: Tyseley
Length of Line: One third of a mile

Nº of Steam Locos: Varies with visiting Locos and restoration contracts
Nº of Members: Approximately 600
Approx Nº of Visitors P.A.: 10,000
Gauge: Standard
Web site: www.tyseleylocoworks.co.uk

GENERAL INFORMATION

Nearest Mainline Station: Tyseley (5 mins. walk)
Nearest Bus Station: Birmingham. Bus Stop at Reddings Lane – 2 minutes walk (Bus route 37 passes the entrance)
Car Parking: 200 spaces at Railway site
Coach Parking: Space at Railway site
Souvenir Shop(s): Yes
Food & Drinks: None

SPECIAL INFORMATION

The Museum runs a large workshop which produces refurbished locomotives, many for operation on Network Rail Lines.

OPERATING INFORMATION

Opening Times: An open weekend is to be held during the June 2017. Please contact Tyseley for further details of this event.
Steam Working: On all open days. The Loco Works also operates mainline excursions from the Museum Station and runs the Shakespeare Express from Birmingham to Stratford-upon-Avon every Sunday from 16th July to 3rd September 2017.
Prices: Shakespeare Express fares start from around £30.00 for adults and £20.00 for children (age 5 to 15) but tickets are cheaper if purchased in advance. Fares shown are for return tickets from Birmingham stations and Henley. Returns from Stratford are cheaper.

Detailed Directions by Car:
From the North: Exit the M6 at Junction 6 and take A41 ring road towards Solihull; From the South: Exit the M42 at Junction 5 and take the A41 towards Birmingham.

THE WEARDALE RAILWAY

Address: Stanhope Station, Stanhope, Bishop Auckland   DL13 2YS
Telephone Nº: (01388) 526203
Year Formed: 1993
Location: Stanhope to Witton-le-Wear, County Durham
Length of Line: 13 miles

Nº of Steam Locos: 1
Nº of Other Locos: 4 (including DMUs)
Nº of Members: 850
Gauge: Standard
Web site: www.weardale-railway.org.uk

GENERAL INFORMATION

Nearest Mainline Station: Bishop Auckland (¼ mile)
Nearest Bus Station: Bishop Auckland
Car Parking: Available at both Stanhope and Wolsingham Stations
Coach Parking: Available at Wolsingham Station
Souvenir Shop(s): Yes
Food & Drinks: Yes – Signal Box Cafe, Stanhope

SPECIAL INFORMATION

Weardale is in the heart of the North Pennines and the railway provides magnificent unspoilt views. The area is known for its footpaths and bridleways and the railway provides a useful base for walks between stations along banks of the beautiful River Wear.

OPERATING INFORMATION

Opening Times: 2017 heritage rail services will operate on weekends and bank holidays from Good Friday to 29th October. Services will also operate on Wednesdays and Thursdays from 20th July to 1st September. Trains leave Stanhope from 10.30am or 11.00am depending on the time of the year. Please check the web site for further information when planning a visit.
Steam Working: None at present.
Prices: Adult Return £14.00   Child Return £8.00
                   Concession Return £12.00
                   Family Return £36.00
Note: The prices shown above are for a return journey from Stanhope to Witton-le-Wear and may be subject to change.

Detailed Directions by Car:
From All Parts: Stanhope Station is located in Stanhope, just off the A689; Bishop Auckland West Station is a short walk from the Northern Rail Mainline Station in Bishop Auckland (SatNavs use DL14 7TL).

WENSLEYDALE RAILWAY

Address: Leeming Bar Station, Leases Road, Leeming Bar, Northallerton DL7 9AR **Telephone Nº:** (01677) 425805 **Year Formed:** The railway association was formed in 1990, the Railway PLC in 2000. **Location of Line:** Leeming Bar to Redmire **Length of Line:** Approximately 16 miles	**Nº of Steam Locos:** Visiting locos only **Nº of Other Locos:** Various Diesel locos **Nº of Members:** 3,500 **Annual Membership Fee:** £17.50 **Approx Nº of Visitors P.A.:** Not known **Gauge:** Standard **Web site:** www.wensleydalerail.com

GENERAL INFORMATION

Nearest Mainline Station: Northallerton (7 miles)
Nearest Bus Station: Northallerton (7 miles)
Car & Coach Parking: Available at Leeming Bar, Leyburn and Redmire Stations
Souvenir Shop(s): Yes
Food & Drinks: At Leeming Bar, Bedale & Leyburn stations.

SPECIAL INFORMATION

Most services are operated via DMU and travel to Leyburn & Redmire tourist destinations in the Wensleydale Valley. Other heritage diesel groups also use the line.

OPERATING INFORMATION

Opening Times: 2017 dates: Weekends and Bank Holidays from late February to early November. Tuesdays and most Wednesdays from 11th April to the end of October. Open daily in August (but for Mondays when the railway is closed). A limited timetable operates on weekends in November. Also open for a number of other Special Event Days including Santa Specials in December. Please contact the railway for further information.
Steam Working: Most services are operated by DMU except during the summer months when a visiting steam locomotive should be in operation.
Prices: A variety of single and Day Ticket fares are available at both standard and discounted rates. Please contact the railway for further details.

Detailed Directions by Car:
From All Parts: Exit the A1 at the Leeming Bar exit and take the A684 towards Northallerton. The station is on the left after about ¼ mile close to the road junction and after the traffic lights.   By Bus: The Dales & District 73 bus route travels between Northallerton and Leeming Bar.

WEST SOMERSET RAILWAY

Address: The Railway Station, Minehead, Somerset TA24 5BG	**Nº of Steam Locos**: 6
Telephone Nº: (01643) 704996 (enquiries)	**Nº of Other Locos**: 12
Year Formed: 1976	**Nº of Members**: 3,500
Location of Line: Bishops Lydeard (near Taunton) to Minehead	**Annual Membership Fee**: £20.00
	Approx Nº of Visitors P.A.: 200,000
Length of Line: 19¾ miles	**Gauge**: Standard
	Web site: www.west-somerset-railway.co.uk

GENERAL INFORMATION

Nearest Mainline Station: Taunton (4 miles)
Nearest Bus Station: Taunton (4½ miles) –
Service 28 run to Bishops Lydeard, Watchet,
Washford and Minehead.
Car Parking: Available at all stations except
Doniford Halt. Free parking at Bishops Lydeard.
Coach Parking: As above
Souvenir Shops: Yes – at Minehead, Bishops Lydeard
and Washford. Sales counters at other stations.
Food & Drinks: Yes – At some stations. Buffet cars
on most trains.

SPECIAL INFORMATION

Britain's longest Standard gauge Heritage railway
runs through the Quantock Hills and along the
Bristol Channel Coast. The line passes through no
fewer than ten Stations with museums at Washford
and Blue Anchor and a turntable at Minehead.

OPERATING INFORMATION

Opening Times: 2017 dates: Various dates from
March to December and daily from 16th May to 8th
October. Open 9.30am to 5.30pm. Please contact the
railway for detailed information.
Steam Working: All operating days except during
Diesel Galas.
Prices: Adult Day Rover £20.00
Child Day Rover £10.00 (ages 5 to 17)
Family Rover £49.00 (2 adult + 2 child)
Senior Citizen Day Rover £18.00
Note: Tickets purchased in advance are cheaper

Detailed Directions by Car:
Exit the M5 at Taunton (Junction 25) and follow the A358 towards Minehead. Bishops Lydeard Station is signposted
from the village bypass. The A39 (which the A358 joins at Williton) goes directly past Washford Station. Minehead
Station is on the seafront at the edge of the town centre, approximately ½ miles from Butlins Holiday Centre.

WHITWELL & REEPHAM RAILWAY

Address: Whitwell Road, Reepham, Norfolk NR10 4GA	**Nº of Steam Locos**: 1
Telephone Nº: (01603) 871694	**Nº of Other Locos**: 1
Year Formed: 2009	**Nº of Members**: Approximately 400
Location of Line: Norfolk	**Annual Membership Fee**: £15.00
Length of Line: Almost ½ mile	**Approx Nº of Visitors P.A.**: 6,000
	Gauge: Standard
	Web site: www.whitwellstation.com

GENERAL INFORMATION

Nearest Mainline Station: Norwich (15 miles)
Nearest Bus Station: Norwich (15 miles)
Car Parking: Available on site
Coach Parking: Available
Souvenir Shop(s): Yes
Food & Drinks: Available

SPECIAL INFORMATION

Whitwell & Reepham Station re-opened on the 28th February 2009 nearly 50 years after it was closed to passengers on 2nd March 1959. The intention is to restore the Station to its former glory, re-laying of track and sidings, acquiring rolling stock and setting up a museum relating to the Station and The Midland & Great Northern Railway.

OPERATING INFORMATION

Opening Times: Weekends throughout the year from 10.00am until 5.00pm.
Steam Working: The first Sunday of each month plus a number of other Special Event days. Please contact the railway for further details. Steam services operate from 12.30pm to 4.00pm.
Prices: Adults £2.00
Children £1.00
Family £5.00
Note: Prices shown above are for train rides – admission to the museum is free of charge.

Detailed Directions by Car:
From All Parts: Take the A1067 Norwich to Fakenham Road to Bawdeswell then follow the B1145 to Reepham. The railway is located about 1 mile to the South-west of Reepham and is well-signposted.

YEOVIL RAILWAY CENTRE

Address: Yeovil Junction Station, Stoford, Yeovil BA22 9UU	**Nº of Steam Locos:** 2
	Nº of Other Locos: 3
Telephone Nº: (01935) 410420	**Nº of Members:** 300
Year Formed: 1994	**Annual Membership Fee:** £15.00
Location of Line: Yeovil Junction	**Approx Nº of Visitors P.A.:** 5,000
Length of Line: ¼ mile	**Web site:**
Gauge: Standard	www.yeovilrailway.freeservers.com

GENERAL INFORMATION

Nearest Mainline Station: Yeovil Junction (adjacent)
Nearest Bus Station: A regular bus service runs Monday to Saturday from Yeovil Bus Station (2 miles)
Car Parking: Available on site
Coach Parking: Available nearby
Souvenir Shop(s): Yes
Food & Drinks: Available

SPECIAL INFORMATION

The Visitor Centre is located in a GWR Transfer Shed which was built in 1864.
The centre also runs Driver Experience days.

OPERATING INFORMATION

Opening Times: Open regularly for Steam Train days, Mainline steam visits and other special events from March to October. Also open for Santa Specials in December and for static viewing every Sunday morning from 10.00am until noon. Please contact the Centre for further details of event days.
Steam Working: Numerous operating days throughout the year. Please contact the Centre for further details.
Prices: Adult £7.00
 Child £3.50 (Ages 5 to 15)
One child is admitted free with each paying adult
Note: Prices shown above are for Steam Working days.

Detailed Directions by Car:
The Centre is part of Yeovil Junction Station which is served by South West Trains. By road simply follow the signs to Yeovil Junction Station from Yeovil town centre or from the A37 Dorchester to Yeovil road. The entrance to Yeovil Railway Centre is through the low bridge, half way up the Yeovil Junction Station approach road.
